Developing
Clinical Skills for
Substance Abuse
Counseling

Daniel Yalisove

AMERICAN COUNSELING ASSOCIATION
5999 Stevenson Avenue
Alexandria, VA 22304
www.counseling.org

Developing Clinical Skills for
Substance Abuse Counseling

Copyright © 2010 by the American Counseling Association. All rights reserved. Printed in the United States of America. Except as permitted under the United States Copyright Act of 1976, no part of this publication may be reproduced or distributed in any form or by any means, or stored in a database or retrieval system, without the written permission of the publisher.

10   9   8   7   6   5   4   3   2   1

American Counseling Association
5999 Stevenson Avenue
Alexandria, VA 22304

Director of Publications   Carolyn C. Baker

Production Manager   Bonny E. Gaston

Editorial Assistant   Catherine A. Brumley

Copy Editor   Rachel A. Fending

Cover and text design by Bonny E. Gaston

Library of Congress Cataloging-in-Publication Data
Yalisove, Daniel L.
   Developing clinical skills for substance abuse counseling/Daniel Yalisove.
      p. cm.
Includes bibliographical references and index.
ISBN 978-1-55620-307-7 (alk. paper)
1. Substance abuse—Prevention. 2. Rehabilitation counselors. I. Title.
HV4998.Y35 2010

ACC LIBRARY SERVICES AUSTIN, TX
2009025231

Dedication

To my loving wife, Valentina

Table of Contents

Part 1

Introduction to the Basic Theory and Principles of Substance Abuse Counseling

Part 2

Putting Theory and Principles Into Action: Developing Clinical Skills

Preface

Beginning substance abuse counselors are faced with a number of practical challenges. For example, they must discern what the focus of the session should be, when to be firm and when to be flexible, how to structure a session, and how to end it. This text provides a basic framework for understanding substance abuse counseling and offers exercises for students to develop their counseling skills and to prepare them to master these and other counseling challenges. The book is practical and down to earth; it is meant to help beginning counselors and other mental health professionals quickly adapt to substance abuse and other counseling settings with a large percentage of clients with substance use disorders. Clinical issues unique to clients with substance use disorders are addressed.

The principles, theory, and skills introduced in this book are, by and large, compatible with current substance abuse counseling theories, including 12-step facilitation, cognitive–behavioral therapy, motivational interviewing, methadone maintenance, and integrated treatment. Additionally, the approach is compatible with both harm reduction and abstinence goals. Chapter 7 offers some specific suggestions about how to integrate aspects of cognitive–behavioral therapy, relapse prevention, and 12-step treatment with the approach presented in this text. Chapter 10 includes a discussion of how aspects of integrated treatment can be included in this approach. Regardless of your theoretical viewpoint, I believe that the principles and skills set out in this book will help you improve your clinical proficiency.

As we all know, the addiction field has its share of controversies. Perhaps the biggest debate today regards setting treatment goals for clients with substance abuse disorders. Traditional programs advocate an abstinence goal, whereas, more recently, some addiction professionals have seen harm reduction as an acceptable goal for certain clients. I believe that the appropriate goal for each client should be determined by a properly trained clinician on the basis of the specific circumstances of the treatment situation. Often, the appropriate goal is abstinence; sometimes it is based on harm reduction, such as reduced or safer use of substances or controlled drinking. Thus, I include examples reflecting both abstinence and harm reduction goals. A comprehensive and objective overview of this issue is much needed but beyond the scope of this text.

This book presents an experientially based approach for beginning counselors to develop basic substance abuse counseling skills. Before reading this text, you should have an understanding of substance abuse counseling theory, principles, and knowledge. Two works that fit well with this book and provide the necessary knowledge are by G. Miller (2005) and Jarvis, Tebbutt, Mattick, and Shand (2005). My book *Introduction to Alcohol Research: Implications for Treatment, Prevention, and Policy* (Yalisove, 2004) will give you a good review of the current research knowledge about alcoholism.

Overview of the Book

In Part 1 of the book, the basic principles of substance abuse counseling are clearly formulated, and their rationales are spelled out in a common-sense and practical manner. Part 2 will teach you to apply these principles in clinical situations through the use of experiential exercises and role-plays, which help develop the critical thinking skills that are essential in counseling. In addition, this second part of the book serves as an introduction to the clinical method.

Throughout the text, technical terms are presented in italics and defined on their first use. At the end of this preface is an alphabetical listing of abbreviations used in the text. In addition, I often use metaphors to illustrate concepts. If you don't find them useful, ignore them; you should readily understand the material without them. At the end of most chapters is a section of recommended readings and resources for readers who would like to learn more about the concepts discussed in the chapter.

Each of the chapters includes exercises to help you understand the principles and develop the skills discussed in the chapter. Some of the exercises are to be done individually, and others are done in a role-play format. If the text is being used for a substance abuse counseling course, the role-plays can be done in class in teams or by selected students in front of the class. As you perform the exercises and role-plays, it is important to learn to *self-reflect* on your experiences. That is, try to objectively look back at what you have just done. Good counselors review their clinical work to see where they were successful, where they had difficulty, what worked, and what didn't work. They then can refine their approach to become more proficient. You can use the exercises and role-plays to develop your self-reflective capacity.

Appendix B presents a good format for performing, recording, and analyzing the role-plays. It is closely tied to the Building Session Goals and Strategies (BSGS) approach developed in the text and should help you self-reflect. If you would like to do the role-plays but are reading the text on your own, seek out a few colleagues and an experienced supervisor to help you perform and analyze them.

The following sections provide a brief description of each chapter of the book.

Chapter 1: The Substance Abuse Counselor

This chapter describes the role of the substance abuse counselor; the major tasks of his or her job; the knowledge, skills, and attitudes necessary for a counselor to do well; and the pros and cons of becoming a counselor. The clinical method is introduced, along with BSGS.

Chapter 2: Theoretical Considerations

In this chapter, I discuss the theories the text uses: motivational interviewing, the Stages of Change Model, BSGS, and the eight-stage process of counseling; the latter two are my inventions. Additionally, I discuss the common factors approach to understanding the curative aspects of counseling.

Chapter 3: Some Basic Principles of Substance Abuse Counseling

In this chapter, I review some fundamental principles that are common to all kinds of counseling. First, counselors must educate their clients about what counseling is and what role both counselor and client should play. Counselors need to know their role and their limits. They should understand the diagnosis of substance use disorders and know how to skillfully use this information to motivate the client. Counselors should develop a sense of timing in sessions with clients, and they should be able to determine what goals are most essential to work on in each stage of treatment.

Chapter 4: Applying the Principles of Building Session Goals and Strategies (BSGS) to Prepare for a Session With a Client

This chapter focuses on how to use BSGS principles to organize and focus sessions with clients. You will learn how to determine a specific goal for the session, how to choose techniques to achieve the goal, and how to evaluate whether you were successful. Included in the chapter is an extensive list of techniques you can use, along with brief descriptions. At the end of the chapter is an important discussion about the challenge of being flexible as a counselor while maintaining the goals that you feel are appropriate.

Chapter 5: Building Session Goals and Strategies (BSGS) and the First Session

The focus of this chapter is on how to apply the principles of BSGS to the first session. Appropriate goals and strategies are discussed, and the concepts of empathy, operational empathy, and reflection are introduced.

Chapter 6: Beyond the First Session: The Beginning Phase of Treatment

In this chapter, the focus is on getting started to help the client. The first phase of counseling includes a "getting to know you" aspect; the counselor's goals are to evaluate the client's motivation to change and build his or her motivation. This chapter also includes a discussion of two important issues in substance abuse treatment: keeping track of the client's drug use with routine queries and toxicology tests, and considerations in treating mandated clients.

Chapter 7: The Middle Phase of Treatment

If the client has made good progress, in the middle phase of treatment the counselor can introduce new goals and use different techniques from the opening phase of treatment. The following techniques are discussed: relapse prevention; coping skills training; the 12-step facilitation approach to the middle phase of treatment and the use of other self-help; examination of clients' lifestyle, goals, and career; exploration of factors associated with substance abuse; and early discussions about termination.

Chapter 8: Moving Toward Termination

The termination phase is a dynamic and important aspect of treatment. This process is complicated by the fact that most substance abuse treatment ends before all goals are achieved. The chapter discusses the following topics related to termination: the emotional factors experienced by both client and counselor in termination, criteria for successful termination, circumstances of termination, the stages of change and termination, how to prepare clients to continue on their own, and how to say goodbye.

Chapter 9: Group Counseling for Clients With Substance Use Disorders

This chapter focuses on interactional group counseling for substance abusers. The basic elements, guidelines for leadership, the basic processes of change, and special techniques of group counseling are discussed. The chapter emphasizes the importance of recognizing the highly emotional aspects of group process and dealing with them therapeutically.

Chapter 10: The Role of the Substance Abuse Counselor in the Treatment of Clients With Both Substance Use Disorders and Mental Disorders

This chapter discusses the specific role that the substance abuse counselor can play in the treatment of clients with dual disorders. Topics include monitoring psychiatric symptoms, medication compliance, and mental health treatment compliance as well as educating the client about psychiatric symptoms as a trigger of substance abuse relapse. The chapter also gives an introduction to integrated treatment, an empirically supported approach for treating clients with substance abuse disorders and severe mental illness. Harm reduction as a treatment goal is also discussed.

Chapter 11: Working With the Significant Others of Clients With Substance Use Disorders

The basic principles of working with the significant others of clients with substance use disorders are discussed in this chapter. Therapeutic goals include reducing the maladaptive behavior of the significant other, increasing the significant other's self-care capacity, and encouraging the partner with the substance use disorder to accept treatment. The chapter also outlines how to assess the potential for violence in the family and create a safety plan when necessary. Community reinforcement and family training, a systematic approach for helping the significant others of people with substance use disorders, is summarized in the chapter.

Chapter 12: Considerations of Diversity in Substance Abuse Counseling

The basic principles developed in the book are complementary to an enlightened view of diversity. In multicultural counseling, one's awareness of one's own feelings, beliefs, and thought processes is an important ingredient in the provision of effective interventions for clients whose background is different from one's own. After a brief review of ethical considerations, the concept of multicultural competence is addressed, and its relationship to empathy and the therapeutic relationship is developed. The following specific populations of substance abusers are discussed: women; African Americans; Latino/as; Native Americans; Asian Americans; clients with a disability, an unusual physical appearance, or a serious illness; gay, lesbian, bisexual, and transgendered clients; and recent immigrants.

Chapter 13: Treatment Plans and Clinical Writing

In this chapter, clinical writing is discussed. Substance abuse counselors must write a number of reports; this chapter describes the major kinds, including psychosocial narratives, admission and discharge summaries, treatment plans, and progress notes. Detailed examples of each kind of report are provided.

I have also adapted BSGS, a basic approach for planning a counseling session, to the task of creating client treatment plans. In BSGS, students learn to determine the appropriate goal for a session, develop techniques for achieving it, and evaluate the session's outcome. This approach can help students develop client treatment plans, which involves formulating longer term goals.

Chapter 14: Closing Perspective

In this chapter, I provide some practical advice for the new counselor, including tips on how to survive at one's first job and information about obtaining the substance abuse counseling credential. I also discuss some resources to continue your education in the areas of professional ethics, work with adolescents, research knowledge in substance abuse, and theories of substance abuse counseling.

Answer Guide

The answer guide provides answers to some of the exercises.

Instructor's Guide

An Instructor's Guide for *Developing Clinical Skills for Substance Abuse Counseling* can be dowloaded from the American Counseling Association's online bookstore at http://www.counseling.org/Publications.

Appendixes

This text includes three appendixes. Appendix A lists the Technical Assistance Publication Series 21 counseling competencies (Center for Substance Abuse Treatment, 2006) covered in the text and in which chapter each is discussed. Appendix B presents the role-play recording form for students whose instructors are using the workbook log. Appendix C consists of the Alcohol Use Disorders Identification Test (Babor, Biddle, Saunders, & Monteiro, 2001) and Drug Abuse Screening Test (Skinner, 1982).

List of Abbreviations Used in the Text

- AA: Alcoholics Anonymous
- AUDIT: Alcohol Use Disorders Identification Test (Babor et al., 2001)
- BSGS: Building Session Goals and Strategies
- CBT: Cognitive–behavioral therapy
- CRAFT: Community Reinforcement and Family Training
- CSO: Concerned significant other
- DAST-20: Drug Abuse Screening Test (Skinner, 1982)
- *DSM–IV–TR: Diagnostic and Statistical Manual of Mental Disorders* (4th ed., text rev.; American Psychiatric Association, 2000)
- GLBT: Gay, lesbian, bisexual, and transgendered
- MI: Motivational interviewing
- NA: Narcotics Anonymous
- PTSD: Posttraumatic stress disorder
- SMI: Serious mental illness
- SUD SO: Significant other with a substance use disorder
- TAP 21: Technical Assistance Publication Series 21 (Center for Substance Abuse Treatment, 2006)
- TAU: Treatment as usual

Readings and Resources

Jarvis, T. J., Tebbutt, J., Mattick, R. P., & Shand, F. (2005). *Treatment approaches for alcohol and drug dependence: An introductory guide.* Hoboken, NJ: Wiley.

This excellent advanced text on substance abuse counseling discusses all of the current substance abuse counseling theories.

Miller, G. (2005). *Learning the language of addiction counseling* (2nd ed.). Hoboken, NJ: Wiley.

This is a basic text on substance abuse counseling.

Yalisove, D. L. (2004). *Introduction to alcohol research: Implications for treatment, prevention, and policy.* Boston: Allyn & Bacon.

This book provides a good review of relevant research pertaining to substance abuse treatment, prevention, and policy.

Acknowledgments

The approach presented in this text evolved from my efforts to teach substance abuse counseling skills in an advanced course for addiction studies students over the past decade at John Jay College. I am grateful to those students who were enthusiastic and persistent, tolerated my missteps, and provided vital feedback for the text. The 2007–2008 research fellowship leave granted by John Jay College afforded me the time to write the text.

In addition, I wish to thank my editor, Carolyn Baker, who has provided consistent and invaluable assistance in guiding me through the process of publishing this book. Finally, I gratefully acknowledge Kim Mueser's helpful and sensitive critique of Chapter 10. Although I incorporated many of his suggestions, I take sole responsibility for the views expressed in the chapter.

About the Author

Daniel Yalisove, PhD, is an associate professor of psychology at John Jay College of Criminal Justice. He has been the coordinator of the addiction studies program since 1993 and has taught a variety of addiction studies courses during this time. He created and developed the curriculum for the program, which both is evidence based and provides skills training for its students. His current interest is improving pedagogy in addiction studies, and he has published several papers on this topic. He is active in the International Coalition for Addiction Studies Education and currently serves as its secretary.

Dr. Yalisove received his doctorate in clinical psychology at New York University in 1975. He completed advanced training in psychoanalysis at the New York University Postdoctoral Program and graduated in 1983. He earned the credential in substance abuse counseling in 1980.

Dr. Yalisove has worked in the substance abuse field since 1976, when he began his association with Cabrini Medical Center in New York City. He was the program director of the Cabrini Alcoholism Program from 1980 to 1992. During this period, he supervised substance abuse counselors, provided education on substance abuse to psychiatric residents, and offered direct service to clients with substance use disorders. He also implemented an innovative acupuncture outpatient detoxification program modeled after Dr. Michael Smith's program at Lincoln Hospital in the Bronx.

In addition, Dr. Yalisove edited the *Essential Papers on Addiction,* published in 1997. This volume draws together the clinically relevant psychoanalytic writings on addiction. His second book was *Introduction to Alcohol Research: Implications for Treatment, Prevention, and Policy,* which reviews the relevant research for treatment, prevention, and policy regarding alcohol problems and disorders.

Dr. Yalisove is married and lives in New York City and Pushkin, Russia. He is an amateur jazz clarinet player and plays occasional gigs around town.

About the Contributors

Richard Kempter, PhD, received his doctorate in educational psychology from the University of Michigan. He worked for 15 years as a prison psychologist in the Michigan Department of Corrections and has extensive training and experience in running counseling groups. He was a trainer for T-Groups and a family systems therapist at the University of Michigan. He is currently the psychologist and manager for a therapeutic community treating substance abuse, homelessness, and mental illness at Bellevue Hospital in New York City and an adjunct instructor at John Jay College of Criminal Justice, teaching in the addiction studies program.

Errol O. Rodriguez, PhD, CRC, is the director of the Family and Youth Addiction Program at Jacobi Medical Center in New York and an adjunct assistant professor at John Jay College of Criminal Justice's Addiction Studies Program. In addition, Dr. Rodriguez holds adjunct professorships at Ferkauf Graduate School of Psychology at Yeshiva University and the Gordon F. Derner Institute of Advanced Psychological Studies at Adelphi University. He has published in the area of addiction and family and has a private practice in New York City.

Part 1

Introduction to the Basic Theory and Principles of Substance Abuse Counseling

Chapter 1

The Substance Abuse Counselor

This chapter describes the role of the substance abuse counselor; his or her major tasks; and the knowledge, skills, and attitudes he or she needs to do well. It also discusses the pros and cons of becoming a counselor. The clinical method is introduced, along with the Building Session Goals and Strategies (BSGS) approach.

What Does a Counselor Do?

Substance abuse counselors work as part of a treatment team in a variety of clinical settings, including detoxification programs, both inpatient and outpatient treatment programs, methadone maintenance programs, and therapeutic communities. Most of these settings subscribe to a specific treatment philosophy, such as 12-step facilitation or cognitive–behavioral therapy (CBT), and their goals are abstinence or harm reduction.

Substance abuse counselors help clients overcome substance use disorders. They offer individual and group counseling as well as other interventions. They must interact cooperatively with a variety of other counselors and clinical staff to provide clients with an environment that facilitates change. How do counselors help their clients? Of course, the treatment philosophy of each program gives direction about the kinds of interventions that are helpful. For example, a 12-step facilitation program introduces clients to the 12 steps and encourages participation in Alcoholics Anonymous (AA) or Narcotics Anonymous (NA). Other factors that help clients change are common to all kinds of treatment. One such factor is interpersonal skills, which counselors can use to foster a good therapeutic relationship with their clients (Lambert & Barley, 2002). This text is largely focused on the helping processes that are common to most kinds of substance abuse treatment, especially developing the interpersonal skills of counselors. Another aspect of the counselor's role is to document client information and contact in a number of ways, commonly referred to as *paperwork*. This is discussed in Chapter 13.

If one has no substance abuse counseling experience, what in one's own life experience can provide an insight into the process of helping clients overcome substance abuse? Perhaps the clearest analogy is that a substance abuse counselor is like a good teacher. Students come to instructors to learn something. They hope to become proficient in their subject matter, whether it is swimming, speaking French, playing the flute, or counseling. A flute teacher is not responsible for making his or her student a good flute player. That depends on the student's motivation, practice, and inborn talent. The teacher is responsible for showing the student how to play the instrument, providing a good practice plan, and pointing out flaws in the student's playing so that he or she can improve. A teacher can build motivation to practice in a number of ways. He or she can give encouragement and point out improvements that are hard for the student to see. When a teacher has provided all the assistance he or she can, he or she should say so and either recommend another teacher or suggest that the student's flute education is complete. Similarly, a substance abuse counselor cannot cure the client of his or her substance use disorder but can only inspire, motivate, encourage, and provide direction.

The Clinical Method

To foster a *critical thinking* process for students so they can learn to adapt clinical principles to the specific clinical situation at hand, I have developed a process called BSGS. This process provides an introduction to the clinical method. In the BSGS approach, students develop a goal for the counseling session, derive techniques to foster the goal, and evaluate whether the goal was achieved. There are two alternatives to this approach, neither of which I believe is satisfactory:

1. The counselor can follow a treatment manual with no flexibility. For example, imagine that in the previous session the counselor had given a specific homework assignment to a client. The client comes in for the session distraught about having just lost his job. If the counselor strictly follows the treatment manual, he or she will focus on the homework. How do you think the client would feel?
2. The counselor can respond to his or her client intuitively, reacting on gut feelings. For example, a counselor may have the first impression that his or her client is an alcoholic in denial and react to that immediately, confronting the client. Clearly, there may be some problems if, in the first session with a client, the counselor says, "It's clear to me that you are an alcoholic in denial."

Neither approach allows counselors much chance for *self-reflection* so they can learn from each clinical experience they have. In the first case, counselors simply determine whether they have followed the specified procedure. In the second, they react intuitively, so they lack a process of decision making and thus do not have the tools to self-reflect on their clinical work. One of the main objectives for the role-play exercises in this book is to help students learn to self-reflect about their experiences in doing the role-plays.

What Are the Knowledge, Attitudes, and Skills Required for Substance Abuse Counseling?

The knowledge, attitudes, and skills required for substance abuse counseling are spelled out in *Addiction Counseling Competencies: The Knowledge, Skills, and Attitudes of Professional Practice* (Technical Assistance Publication Series 21 [TAP 21]; Center for Substance Abuse Treatment, 2006). The book is broken into two broad sections; the first of these, Transdisciplinary Foundations, refers to knowledge about substance use disorders. The four areas listed in this section are

- understanding addiction,
- treatment knowledge,
- application to practice, and
- professional readiness.

The second section is called The Professional Practice of Addiction Counseling and addresses eight *practice dimensions:*

- clinical evaluation;
- treatment planning;
- referral;
- service coordination;
- counseling;
- client, family, and community education;
- documentation; and
- professional and ethical responsibilities.

Within each of these dimensions, competencies are listed, with knowledge, skill, and attitude components. Appendix A presents the TAP 21 competencies covered in the text and lists in which chapter each is discussed.

Who Should Become a Substance Abuse Counselor?

You may be wondering whether the substance abuse counseling profession is the right one for you. There are no absolute rules about this. My view is that if a person wants to help people and is patient, observant, and sympathetic; open to his or her own feelings; and accepting of others' feelings, that person is a candidate for becoming a good counselor. One must also have an empathic and nonjudgmental attitude toward clients struggling with substance use disorders. One needn't be a genius. One does, however, need to be motivated. Counseling work brings with it a lot of potential frustrations, and it is not a high-paying profession. It should be something one wants to do.

Readings and Resources

Center for Substance Abuse Treatment. (2006). *Addiction counseling competencies: The knowledge, skills, and attitudes of professional practice* (Technical Assistance Publication Series 21, DHHS Publication No. SMA 06-4171). Rockville, MD: Substance Abuse and Mental Health Services Administration.
This text describes the competencies addiction counselors should have.

Exercises

E.1.1. Teachers

Think about your best and worst teachers—what they were like and how they taught—and you can see a clear analogy to good and bad counseling attitudes and techniques. Who was your best teacher? What was he or she like? Why do you feel that teacher was the best? What qualities did he or she have and what techniques did he or she use that facilitated your learning? Which qualities and techniques would you like to incorporate into your counseling approach, and why?

Who was your worst teacher? What was he or she like? Why do you feel that teacher was the worst? What qualities did he or she have and what techniques did he or she use that prevented you from learning? Which qualities and techniques would you be sure not to incorporate into your counseling approach? (Note that this will be your first log entry if you are keeping a log.)

Chapter 2

Theoretical Considerations

In this chapter, I discuss the theories this text is based on: motivational interviewing (MI), the Stages of Change Model, Building Session Goals and Strategies (BSGS), and the eight-stage process of counseling; the latter two are my inventions. Additionally, the text uses the common factors approach to understanding curative aspects of counseling.

This book is based on the view that certain curative factors in substance abuse counseling are common to all theories of substance abuse treatment (Moos, 2007). Research to date in substance abuse counseling outcomes (Morgenstern & McKay, 2007; Najavits, Crits-Christoph, & Dierberger, 2000) as well as psychotherapy research outcomes (Lambert & Barley, 2002) shows few differences among various kinds of treatment. Individual counselor factors seem to be more important in determining outcome (Horvath & Bedi, 2002). This consistent finding has led a group of psychologists to focus on atheoretical or common factors rather than substance abuse treatment theories to explain outcomes.

The most commonly cited factor is the quality of the relationship between the counselor and the client (Lambert & Barley, 2002; Najavits et al., 2000). As Hubble, Duncan, and Miller (1999) observed, "If the client's view of the relationship is favorable, change is more likely to occur" (p. 412). Counselors' interpersonal relationship skills are, therefore, associated with their ability to form a good therapeutic relationship (Horvath & Bedi, 2002). Other common factors linked to positive outcomes include providing appropriate education in the treatment process (Arnkoff, Glass, & Shapiro, 2002), creating a focus and structure for the sessions (Hubble et al., 1999), and breaking down goals into manageable steps (Hubble et al., 1999). This text focuses on helping students and beginning counselors develop these and similar skills.

Additionally, the text combines four basic therapeutic approaches:

- MI,
- the Stages of Change Model,
- BSGS, and
- the eight-stage process of therapy.

I use these approaches to give the reader a framework in which to think about the tasks of substance abuse counseling and to foster the interpersonal skills that will help counselors develop a good working relationship with their clients. I view these approaches as largely common factors; that is, they can be applied to most theoretical perspectives.

Diagnosis of Substance Use Disorders

It is important for substance abuse counselors to understand how to accurately diagnose substance use disorders, even if they cannot officially make a diagnosis. The *Diagnostic and Statistical Manual of Mental Disorders (DSM)* of the American Psychiatric Association is the standard reference for determining the diagnosis of mental disorders. Because the *DSM* is periodically revised, counselors should consult the latest edition for diagnostic criteria. The fourth edition, text revision (*DSM–IV–TR;* American Psychiatric Association, 2000), provides the current method of diagnosis. Regardless of the substance used, substance use disorders are divided into two categories: substance abuse and substance dependence. When diagnosing a specific disorder, the counselor uses the name of the substance as part of the diagnosis. Thus, if a person meets the criteria for substance abuse in his or her use of cocaine, the diagnosis is cocaine abuse. For additional diagnostic considerations, see the *DSM–IV–TR* and Yalisove (2004). The *DSM–IV–TR* criteria for substance abuse and substance dependence follow.

Substance Abuse

A. A maladaptive pattern of substance use leading to clinically significant impairment or distress, as manifested by one (or more) of the following, occurring within a 12-month period.
   (1) Recurrent substance use resulting in a failure to fulfill major role obligations at work, school, or home (e.g., repeated absences or poor work performance related to substance use; substance-related absences, suspensions, or expulsion from school; neglect of children or household)
   (2) Recurrent substance use in situations in which it is physically hazardous (e.g., driving an automobile or operating a machine when impaired by substance use)

(3) Recurrent substance-related legal problems (e.g., arrests for substance-related disorderly conduct)

(4) Continued substance use despite having persistent or recurrent social or interpersonal problems caused or exacerbated by the effects of the substance (e.g., arguments with spouse about consequences of intoxication, physical fights)

B. The symptoms have never met the criteria for Substance Dependence for this class of substance.

Substance Dependence

A. A maladaptive pattern of substance use leading to clinically significant impairment or distress, as manifested by three (or more) of the following, occurring at any time in the same 12-month period.

(1) Tolerance, as defined by either of the following:

(a) A need for markedly increased amounts of the substance to achieve intoxication or desired effect.

(b) Markedly diminished effect with continued use of the same amount of the substance.

(2) Withdrawal, as manifested by either of the following:

(a) The characteristic withdrawal syndrome for the substance (refer to criteria A and B of the criteria sets for withdrawal from the specific substances).

(b) The same (or closely related) substance is taken to relieve or avoid withdrawal symptoms.

(3) The substance is often taken in larger amounts or over a longer period than was intended.

(4) There is a persistent desire or unsuccessful efforts to cut down or control substance use.

(5) A great deal of time is spent in activities necessary to obtain the substance (e.g., visiting multiple doctors or driving long distances), to use the substance (e.g., chain smoking), or recovering from its effects.

(6) Important social, occupational, or recreational activities are given up or reduced because of substance use.

(7) The substance use is continued despite knowledge of having a persistent or recurrent physical or psychological problem that is likely to have been caused or exacerbated by the substance (e.g., current cocaine use despite recognition of cocaine-induced depression, or continued drinking despite recognition that an ulcer was made worse by alcohol consumption.)[1]

---

[1]Reprinted with permission from the *Diagnostic and Statistical Manual of Mental Disorders,* Text Revision, Fourth Edition, (Copyright 2000). American Psychiatric Association.

Motivational Interviewing

MI is a popular approach in substance abuse counseling. It was developed by W. R. Miller and Rollnick (1991, 2002) and has been applied in many treatment settings, with a great deal of research conducted on its effectiveness. MI combines principles of Rogerian client-centered therapy, including the use of empathy, genuineness, and reflection, with modifications to increase clients' motivation to change their addictive behaviors. It also draws on the Stages of Change Model, which is outlined below. The following is a brief summary of the basic elements of MI.

Empathy

The concept of empathy is a major principle of client-centered counseling (Bohart, Elliott, Greenberg, & Watson, 2002) and has been adapted for use in MI. The major consideration is that counselors can be more helpful to clients if they are empathic. That is, if counselors can put themselves in the client's shoes and get a good sense of what the client is feeling, thinking, and concerned about, they are more likely to engage the client constructively. Truly feeling the empathy (Sellman, MacEwan, Deering, & Adamson, 2007) is critical; the demonstration usually follows relatively easily. That is, if counselors feel empathic toward a client, they can show that empathy to the client in a natural and genuine way.

Research summarized by W. R. Miller and Rollnick (1991, 2002) indicates that empathic counselors' clients are more likely to become and remain sober than nonempathic counselors' clients. Bohart et al.'s (2002) review of the psychotherapy outcome literature suggests that counselor empathy is at least as important as the kind of treatment provided. Empathy is a vital element in promoting a good therapeutic relationship with the client. Research has shown that outcomes in substance abuse treatment are enhanced when a good relationship exists between the counselor and client (Belding, Iguchi, Morral, & McLellan, 1997; Bell, Montoya, & Atkinson, 1997; Joe, Simpson, Dansereau, & Rowan-Szal, 2001; Kasarabada, Hser, Boles, & Yu, 2002).

Genuineness means acting and talking in an honest manner. The counselor's comments to the client should reflect what the counselor really feels. When one is demonstrating empathy, it is important not to exaggerate or be phony.

One way of demonstrating empathy is by *reflecting* back what one thinks the client means. This means not parroting or echoing what the client says but creatively and accurately distilling the important aspects of what he or she is experiencing. For example, if the client seems to be distressed about his or her drug use, the counselor could reflect, "Your drug use pattern really seems to bother you."

Note that the example illustrates two hallmarks of MI: focusing on the client's feelings rather than saying the drug use is bad ("bother you"), and making a tentative formulation ("seems to bother you") rather than an authoritative statement. Reflection may seem simple, but it can be used creatively and effectively as a way of underlining and emphasizing important motivation and developing awareness in the client.

A critical MI principle is that it is the counselor's responsibility to build motivation when the client is not yet engaged in the process of change. This idea is discussed in Chapter 6.

Acceptance of Ambivalence

Finally, another important principle of MI is accepting clients' ambivalence about their use of substances (W. R. Miller & Rollnick, 2002). MI accepts that ambivalence is a common human experience. After all, everyone has difficulty making decisions from time to time. Many people struggle over whether to end or commit to a relationship or to change careers. Thus, the MI approach acknowledges that many clients may simultaneously want to continue to use addictive substances and also want to stop. Rather than focusing on the reasons the client should stop, the MI counselor reflects the client's ambivalence back to him or her, allowing the client to see the pros and cons of use. If counselors just emphasize the negative aspects, one side of the ambivalence, it is likely that clients will switch to the other side of the ambivalence and focus on the pros of drug use.

In the following example, the counselor focuses on the bad things about alcohol use:

Joe: I know that drinking is not good for me. It's ruining my relationship with my girlfriend, and my doctor says I should stop drinking because I'm developing liver problems. But I really enjoy drinking with my buddies. It's like my second family. I don't really know what to do.
Counselor: Drinking is causing you a lot of harm. You really should stop.
Joe: You're probably right, but I really enjoy it.

Alternatively, the counselor could focus on the client's ambivalence, saying, "It sounds like it's hard for you to figure out what to do about your drinking."

Recall instances when you had ambivalent feelings about something: a boyfriend or girlfriend or a job, for example. Recall your discussions with friends who tried to help you make a decision. Do you recall some friends emphasizing one choice over the other? Do you recall your response? Typically, when this happens, the ambivalent person focuses on the other side of the ambivalence. So if a friend extols the virtues of a woman's boyfriend, whom the woman feels ambivalent about, the woman will likely counter her friend's argument by listing all of the boyfriend's negative aspects. This is known as *reactance* (W. R. Miller & Rollnick, 1991).

The Stages of Change

The Stages of Change Model was developed to explain basic aspects of the change process. Prochaska, DiClemente, and Norcross (1992) observed people who eventually gave up addictive behavior and saw that they went through stages of readiness to change before they succeeded in changing. The stages are listed below, along with brief examples:

1. In the first stage, *precontemplation,* people are not aware that they have a problem with alcohol or drugs and have no intention to change. They may be defensive about discussing the problem and are often viewed by traditional treatment approaches as unmotivated or in denial (Prochaska, 1999). Family, friends, and employers, however, are usually aware of the problem and may pressure precontemplators to get treatment (Prochaska et al., 1992).

For example, Mary has been using cocaine for a few months and enjoys the high she gets. She believes she can stop anytime she wants to; she just doesn't want to. Her mother is concerned about Mary's use, however.

2. In the second stage, *contemplation,* people with substance use disorders are aware of their problem and are considering change but have made no commitment to change. In this stage, people begin to feel ambivalence about their use of drugs or alcohol (Prochaska, 1999). Contemplators are aware of the negative consequences of their use but still see its positive aspects and often are concerned about how difficult it might be to stop. Contemplators endorse statements such as, "I have a problem, and I really think I should work on it" (Prochaska et al., 1992). Although such statements reflect the contemplator's concern about his or her drug use, they do not necessarily mean that he or she is ready to make a commitment to stop.

In the contemplation stage, Mary continues to use cocaine regularly. She still enjoys the high, but she doesn't like the crash after the high is gone. She is also beginning to be concerned about the drug's cost. She realizes it might be better for her to stop, but she is concerned that it might be quite difficult to do so.

3. In the third stage, *preparation,* the person with a substance use disorder intends to take action to stop using alcohol or other drugs in the near future. He or she might have made small changes but has not made sufficient change to alter the destructive pattern of substance use. The person may have a plan of action, such as going to a recovery group, consulting a counselor, or buying a self-help book (Prochaska, 1999).

In this stage, Mary has determined that the costs of using cocaine outweigh the benefits and has decided she must stop using it. She is trying to cut down on her expenditures for cocaine, and she will consult a substance abuse counselor if she is unsuccessful on her own.

4. In the *action* stage, the person with a substance use disorder begins to take the necessary action to overcome the negative alcohol or other drug use and has stopped harmful use of the substance for at least 1 day. The

action phase lasts until the person has successfully ceased the negative substance use behavior for 6 months. People in the action stage endorse statements such as, "Anyone can talk about changing; I am actually doing something about it" (Prochaska et al., 1992).

In the action phase, Mary has entered a treatment program and has been abstinent 1 week. She has told her closest friends that she wants to stop using cocaine.

5. In the *maintenance* phase, the person with a substance use disorder has been in remission from the disorder's symptoms for more than 6 months. He or she must work to prevent relapse and consolidate the gains made in the action stage. As Mark Twain said, "Stopping smoking is easy; I've done it a thousand times." Staying stopped is the hard part.

In the maintenance phase, Mary has been abstinent from cocaine for 6 months. She attends counseling for relapse prevention.

Relapse, Recurrence, and Recycling

Relapse or recurrence occurs when a person resumes the destructive alcohol or other drug use after a period of abstinence or controlled use. Relapse is common among people who eventually overcome their substance use disorder. In fact, most people who try to stop relapse at least once (Prochaska et al., 1992). The relapse may take the person back to any of the stages earlier than maintenance. He or she then can recycle through the stages of change.

I have found it useful to make a distinction between what I call *interrupted use* and a *relapse*. A true relapse, to my way of thinking, occurs when clients have the goal to stop or reduce their use and have succeeded for at least a month. Thus, a relapse may happen when they are in the action or maintenance stage of change. The relapse is usually unplanned and is often triggered by a stressful event. *Interrupted use*, conversely, refers to when people stop their drug use without any commitment to stay stopped. For example, a client may stop drinking to prove to his wife that he is not an alcoholic. He is likely to resume drinking when he feels he has made his point or even sooner. Thus, interrupted drinking belongs in the precontemplation stage.

Another useful distinction is between a lapse and a relapse. A *lapse* refers to a brief episode of drug use (one drink, one or two hits of marijuana; Marlatt, 1985). A *relapse* refers to a lengthy, full-blown episode of out-of-control use. The lapse can be used as a warning signal, whereas the relapse requires attention to the acute problems of active use, possible detoxification, and a plan to resume abstinence.

Because recurrence is common for those in treatment for substance use disorders, counselors must be prepared for it and deal with it constructively. They must learn to react to recurrence in a nonjudgmental way and help the client view it as a learning experience (Marlatt, 1985) after any ensuing crisis is resolved. The client can examine the factors that led to recurrence and make changes accordingly. Techniques for dealing with relapse are discussed in Chapters 4 and 7.

The stages of change provide a practical way to think about where the client is in his or her motivation to change. Knowing the client's stage of change informs the counselor what his or her goals should be for the client and suggests techniques to achieve those goals. Table 4.1, in Chapter 4, illustrates this approach, listing some appropriate motivational strategies for each stage of change.

BSGS: A Framework for Thinking About a Session With a Client

BSGS is my own invention. I believe this approach will help readers with limited or no clinical experience begin to think clinically and function as beginning counselors. The approach has three basic steps:

1. The counselor's first task is to determine the most important thing to accomplish in the session he or she is about to conduct.
2. Then the counselor determines the strategies and techniques that will help him or her achieve this goal.
3. After the session, the counselor evaluates whether he or she accomplished the goal.

The world of chess has just a few grand master players, yet a lot of people enjoy playing chess. Even the grand masters had to start somewhere. Think of this brief outline I have just presented as similar to the rules of chess. In your first games of chess, you can move the pieces properly, and you know that your objective is to capture the king. If you plan moves that are within your knowledge and stay inside your comfort zone, you may not win the game, but you will learn something for the next game.

The three steps of BSGS give counselors a basic structure and method for managing their sessions. Counselors who use this approach can develop a focus and plan for the session so that they do not let sessions lose direction, which would confuse them and their clients. Step 3 of BSGS also helps counselors learn from their experiences in sessions by encouraging them to reflect on the session.

Eight-Stage Counseling Process

Counseling is a process that has several stages, and the counselor's tasks are different at these different stages. To provide an overview of this process, I have developed an eight-stage model of the counseling process.

1. In the first stage, the counselor needs to learn what the client's problem is. In substance abuse treatment, he or she needs to know whether the problem is related to a substance use disorder. Typically, in an initial session, the first question the counselor asks a client is "What brings you here today?"

Often, clients have a good grasp of the problem and can set it out for their counselor. Others, for a variety of reasons, have difficulty articulating the problem. The counselor must find a way to get these clients to discover or articulate the problem. (This is discussed in Chapter 5.)

The counselor also needs to know the context of the problem for the client. He or she must determine the lay of the land for the client, much as generals who fight battles should have a good grasp of the terrain and the layout of the enemy defenses before attacking. In addition, it is helpful to know what is important to the client, what his or her sensitivities are, and what his or her social situation is. This can help the counselor frame interventions in ways that are in tune with the client.

For example, Joe is in the first stage of the counseling process:

Joe: My wife thinks I have a drinking problem.
Counselor: I might be able to help you with that. Tell me about yourself, your wife, and how the drinking fits into the picture.

If Joe is forthcoming and gives the counselor a good picture of his drinking, his relationship, and his wife, the task of Stage 1 is complete. Note that the counselor uses a light touch when referring to drinking rather than assuming that Joe is an alcoholic.

2. Once the counselor understands the client's problems and their context, the next stage is conveying an understanding of the problem to the client. The client will confirm, add to, or correct that understanding. This begins the important process of collaboration and cooperation.

Counselor: So it seems that your wife is concerned about your drinking, but otherwise you are both happy with the relationship. Would it make sense to explore why your wife is concerned about your drinking and get a clear picture of your drinking pattern by taking the AUDIT [Alcohol Use Disorders Identification Test; Babor, Biddle, Saunders, & Monteiro, 2001] alcohol evaluation?

In this example, the counselor has only a preliminary idea of the problem and needs to learn more. Note that the counselor seeks the client's opinion about the next steps for treatment.

3. Having determined the problem, the counselor can then move to the next stage, evaluating the client's motivation to change. That is, how much does the client want to change his or her addictive behavior?

For example, Joe has now taken the AUDIT, and his score indicates that he probably has an alcohol use disorder.

Counselor: The results of the AUDIT test indicate that you drink a good deal more than is typical. The test also shows that the alcohol impairs your relationship with your wife. Do these results make sense to you?

If Joe agrees, the counselor can continue:

> *Counselor:* It would be useful now to get a more complete picture of your drinking and other aspects of your life that might relate to your drinking. Would you be willing to come in and take a number of tests that can give us a good picture of your drinking and its effects on your life?
>
> *Joe:* Okay.

The results of Joe's tests indicate a *DSM–IV–TR* diagnosis of alcohol abuse.

> *Counselor:* How important is it to you to modify your drinking?

If Joe is highly motivated, the counselor can move on. If not, the counselor needs to build Joe's motivation. Building motivation is discussed in Chapter 6.

4. When the counselor feels the client has sufficient motivation to change, he or she should brainstorm with the client to develop a plan to change. For example, the counselor might ask, "What do you think would help you change this?" "What efforts have you made?" "What worked for you?" or "Would you like suggestions?" An alternative approach is to inform the client of the treatment options that are available, discuss the pros and cons of each, and ask the client what he or she wants to do.

For instance, Joe now agrees that he needs to do something about his drinking.

> *Counselor:* Okay, we've decided that you want to see if you can cut down your drinking to safe levels. You will keep track of your drinks. Your goal is to drink no more than 4 drinks per day and no more than 10 per week. If you go over these limits, we will discuss alternative approaches. Would it be a good idea to bring in your wife to discuss this plan?

Note that the counselor asks whether it would be a good idea to bring in Joe's wife, leaving the decision up to the client. The pros and cons can be discussed. The counselor supports the controlled drinking goal because the client has a diagnosis of alcohol abuse. If the diagnosis were alcohol dependence, the counselor would suggest abstinence as the better goal for achieving success.

5. Once a plan is articulated, the counselor should anticipate potential problems, asking, for example, "What could go wrong with the plan?" and "How can we protect against that?"

In the example of Joe, the counselor could ask him whether he might have a problem keeping the log and accurately reporting where, when, and with whom he is likely to overdrink and then discuss a strategy for handling that problem.

6. Once the plan is in place, the counselor's role shifts to that of a good coach, reinforcing progress, making suggestions, anticipating problems, and helping solve those problems. For example, Joe has been keeping to the controlled drinking plan for the past month.

> *Counselor:* Well, how did it go this week, Joe? Let's take a look at the drinking log. [Joe has gone over the limit for the week and had 10 drinks on 1 day.]
> *Counselor:* Tell me about the day you had the 10 drinks. What can we do to keep this from happening again?
> *Joe:* I popped into Mollie's Tavern on the way home. A few of my drinking buddies were happy to see me and treated me to several drinks. I really didn't plan to have more than 4, but I ended up having about 10.
> *Counselor:* For now, it looks like it's not safe for you to go to Mollie's or to hang out with your old drinking buddies. What do you think?

This stage of treatment is the middle phase and is discussed further in Chapter 7.

7. If the client is successful in solving his or her problem (i.e., has been stably abstinent or safely drinking for several months), the counselor needs to prepare the client to continue on his or her own. The counselor can ask questions such as, "What will help you keep this up?" "What could go wrong?" and "How can we protect against that?"

For example, Joe has been drinking safely for 6 months.

> *Counselor:* Now that you've been drinking safely for 6 months, it's time to think about what you've done to make this possible and how to continue on your own.

This stage is discussed further in Chapter 8, which addresses preparation for termination.

8. Finally, the counselor can end the treatment. In this stage, the counselor summarizes the progress of the client, discusses ways for the client to continue his or her success, and anticipates problems. The counselor allows the client to discuss his or her feelings about ending the relationship. The counselor should suggest a follow-up visit or call and state that the door is open and the client can return if he or she needs to. For example, Joe is now ending his counseling sessions after 8 months of treatment and 7 months of drinking safely.

> *Counselor:* Joe, you've come to sessions for 8 months now. When you started, you weren't drinking safely, you wife was concerned about it, and the drinking was hurting your relationship with her. We developed a plan to limit your drinking. Most of the time you were

successful in limiting your drinking. We found that you couldn't go to Mollie's or hang out with your old drinking buddies and drink safely. When you stopped going there, you did fine. Your relationship with your wife has improved. You've done good work; congratulations. For now, I think I've done all I can do to help you. What do you think? How do you feel about leaving? I recommend a follow-up session in a month. Please remember that the door is open. If you have begun to have some trouble with drinking again, please call.

Note that the counselor gives the client positive feedback. This builds self-esteem and confidence.

Readings and Resources

American Psychiatric Association. (2000). *Diagnostic and statistical manual of mental disorders* (4th ed., text rev.). Washington, DC: Author.

The *DSM–IV–TR* lists the various mental disorders and the criteria for diagnosing them. The fifth edition of the *DSM* is planned for publication in May 2012.

Center for Substance Abuse Treatment. (1999). *Enhancing motivation for change in substance use disorder treatment* (Treatment Improvement Protocol Series 35, DHHS Publication No. SMA 99-3354). Rockville, MD: Substance Abuse and Mental Health Services Administration.

This book is available free from the Substance Abuse and Mental Health Services Administration at http://ncadistore.samhsa.gov/catalog/ and provides a good introduction to MI.

DiClemente, C. C. (2003). *Addiction and change: How addictions develop and addicted people recover.* New York: Guilford Press.

This book provides information on the stages of change.

DiClemente, C. C., & Velasquez, M. M. (2002). Motivational interviewing and the stages of change. In W. R. Miller & S. Rollnick (Eds.), *Motivational interviewing* (pp. 201–216). New York: Guilford Press.

This chapter specifically links the stages of change with MI.

Miller, W. R., & Rollnick, S. (1991, 2002). *Motivational interviewing* (1st and 2nd eds.). New York: Guilford Press.

Miller and Rollnick created the concept of MI. The first edition is written in a relaxed, informal, conversational tone. The second edition is more up to date but drier and more academic in tone.

Prochaska, J. O., DiClemente, C. C., & Norcross, J. C. (1992). In search of how people change: Applications to addictive behaviors. *American Psychologist, 47*, 1102–1114.

This is the classic article that introduced the Stages of Change Model.

Yalisove, D. L. (2004). *Introduction to alcohol research: Implications for treatment, prevention, and policy.* Boston: Allyn & Bacon.

Chapter 2 provides detailed instructions on how to make substance use diagnoses.

Exercises

E.2.1. Demonstrate Empathy

In a team role-play in class, each team should choose a problem they can be empathic about. The problem can be real or made up. If it is real, it should be one that all team members feel comfortable discussing, and it should be understood that the role-play can stop if someone does become uncomfortable. In the role-play, one team member tries to be empathic while another team member talks about the problem. A third team member records the person talking about the problem, and a fourth records what the person trying to be empathic says. These records are combined to form a complete, verbatim dialogue. The role-play should be repeated until each team member has played each part.

Note your feelings and other reactions as counselor, as client, and as observer. This will be a part of the workbook log. Be sure that the observers keep a detailed record. The purpose of this exercise is to be empathic. There is no therapeutic goal for the session; the technique is to demonstrate empathy. Underline and label examples of empathic comments in the verbatim dialogue and note the client's reactions to specific empathic and nonempathic comments. Use the role-play form in Appendix B; this is the first role-play exercise.

E.2.2. Reflection in a Role-Play

Use reflection in a role-play to demonstrate empathy and selectively to build motivation. In this team role-play, you may continue with the scenario started in Exercise E.2.1 or begin a new one. This will be a part of the workbook log. Be sure that the observers keep a detailed record. The purpose of this exercise is to make reflections. There is no therapeutic goal for the session. The technique is reflection. Underline and label the reflections and note the client's reaction to specific reflections in the verbatim account. Use the role-play form in Appendix B, and continue to do so for role-play exercises.

E.2.3. Role-Play of Ambivalent Client to Elicit Reactance or Minimize It

As the counselor in a first session, one member in this team role-play should first focus on the client's need to stop using drugs, then try to focus on the ambivalence the client has. The student role-playing the client must show ambivalence about his or her drug use (i.e., be in the contemplation stage). The point of this exercise is to see which approach is more likely to raise resistance. The observers record a verbatim account. This will be a part of the workbook log. Be sure that the observers keep a detailed record. The purpose in the first part of this role-play is to make authoritative comments about the harmfulness of the drug use. This is also the technique. There is no therapeutic goal for the session. Underline and label authoritative comments and the client's reactions in the dialogue. In the second part, the purpose of the role-play is to focus on the client's ambivalence about his or her drug use. This is also the technique. There is no therapeutic goal for the session. Underline and label when the counselor focuses on ambivalence, and note the client's reaction in the dialogue.

E.2.4. Case Study Review for Stage of Change

Review case studies, and determine the stage of change the client is in. Explain your reasoning for the stage you assign the case. Your professor can give you references for case studies of clients with addictive disorders. (A good source is Kelly & Juhnke, 2005, a casebook of clients with addictive disorders.)

Chapter 3

Some Basic Principles of Substance Abuse Counseling

In this chapter, I review some fundamental principles that are common to all schools of counseling. First, the counselor must educate the client about what counseling is and what part the counselor and the client should play. Counselors need to know their role and their limits. They should understand diagnosis of substance use disorders and know how to skillfully use this information to motivate the client. They should develop a sense of timing in sessions with clients. Finally, they need to be able to prioritize what goals are most essential to work on.

Educating the Client

Participating in a counseling session is not a normal social experience. Although the counselor and client are sitting face to face, as in a typical conversation, the protocol, goals, and procedures are quite different in counseling than in a social conversation. One of the counselor's first, most important tasks is to educate the client about the counseling process: the client's role, the counselor's role, what happens, what can be expected, the provisions of counselor confidentiality, and how the process is supposed to work.

One critical aspect of this education is that the counselor should explain the rationale of the kind of counseling he or she is doing or the intervention he or she is recommending. That is, the counselor should explain why he or she is suggesting a specific procedure, treatment, or intervention. Of course, this requires that the counselor have a good understanding of the approaches and procedures first. The more comfortable the counselor is explaining and interpreting the procedures, the easier it will be for the client to accept them. For example, if a client needs detoxification and has never had this treatment, the counselor needs to explain why it is recommended and what the procedure consists of, answering whatever concerns the client may have. In the following hypothetical dialogue, the counselor explains the rationale for detoxification to the client:

Counselor: Mirabel, from what I can see, it seems that you have been drinking very heavily for the last several days. When you don't have a drink for an hour or so, you start to feel very bad, and you start shaking. This probably means that you are beginning to have the symptoms of alcohol withdrawal. Alcohol withdrawal is a serious condition that needs medical attention. I would like you to see Dr. Martinez. She can determine whether you need to go to the hospital. What do you think?

Mirabel: What will they do?

Counselor: You will be given medication to ease your symptoms; the medical staff will be on the lookout for any medical problems that could occur and will give you a thorough physical examination. You will be in a section of the hospital with others who need detox and will get some guidance for what to do after you leave the hospital.

Mirabel: You don't think I'm an alcoholic, do you?

Counselor: Let's not get ahead of ourselves. For now, I'm concerned about your medical condition. We can discuss your use of alcohol when that is taken care of.

Mirabel: How long will it take?

Counselor: It's usually 5 days. It's a voluntary procedure, so if you decide to leave at any time, you will be able to.

Know Your Role and Limits

Counselors should have the knowledge, skills, and desire to help their clients—but that does not mean that they always can. Many factors can come into play that can limit a counselor's effectiveness. Thus, one cannot guarantee a good outcome, even if the client complies with one's advice. Sometimes a counselor will be stumped by a client's dilemma. This is a normal part of the counseling process, however. The counselor doesn't have to know the answer; he or she can say, "I don't know." Counselors can problem solve with their clients, and they can also seek help from supervisors and colleagues to solve the problem.

The counselor's responsibility is to enlist the client's cooperation, build his or her motivation, and provide help once he or she is motivated to overcome the substance use disorder. If the counselor is unable to do this, he or she must acknowledge it and work with the client to provide the appropriate referral.

It is worth remembering that counselors do not make clients sober. We cannot control our clients, and we are not responsible for their behavior—they are. We can provide guidance, education, and suggestions and can help them get sober. We can teach relapse prevention, but we cannot prevent relapses.

Although we should be warm and friendly, we must also set appropriate boundaries, both to be respectful to our clients and to protect ourselves from potentially difficult situations. I do not recommend lending clients money, granting special favors, giving out personal phone numbers, or meeting clients in social situations. Such actions confuse the nature of the professional relationship and can create practical and ethical difficulties for both the counselor and the client. This issue is covered more completely in professional ethics courses (e.g., see Welfel, 2006).

Some Diagnostic Considerations

Counselors need to understand the substance use disorder diagnoses described in the most recent *DSM,* currently the *DSM–IV–TR* (American Psychiatric Association, 2000), as defined in Chapter 2. How relevant are these diagnoses for the client's treatment? Perhaps the most important aspect of the diagnosis is that it helps determine the appropriate treatment and goals. For example, clients with an alcohol abuse diagnosis may be able to successfully control their drinking, whereas clients with alcohol dependence rarely are able to do so (Yalisove, 2004). Thus, a treatment goal of abstinence is appropriate for clients with alcohol dependence, and clients with alcohol abuse may have the goal of controlling their drinking.

A large percentage of clients in substance abuse treatment have additional psychiatric disorders. Therefore, all substance abuse clients should be screened for psychiatric disorders and appropriately diagnosed. Those with additional psychiatric disorders require additional treatment considerations. This issue is taken up in Chapter 10.

From the MI perspective, it is not a good idea to insist that the client accept the diagnosis he or she is given. It is human nature to avoid painful aspects of one's life, and the counselor who confronts them head on will meet with resistance. The MI approach gives clients a chance to see these painful realities for themselves and come to accept them. Thus, the MI philosophy is not to label the client with a substance use diagnosis.

Timing in Sessions

In addition to specific goals and techniques, counselors need to keep in mind that their sessions are time-limited. They need to think about opening the session, doing the important work, and preparing to end the session. Each session should include the following:

1. A short opening, orienting statement that includes a concise summary of the previous session, discussion of homework, and a specific agenda if there is one for the session. A brief discussion of how the client is doing should follow. On the basis of this information, the counselor decides what needs to be the focus of the session.
2. The heart of the session comes next, when the major current issues are discussed and addressed.
3. In the last 15 minutes, the counselor should begin to "wind down" the session. If the client is emotional, the counselor should help him or her calm down; if there is a crisis, the counselor should begin to discuss practical next steps. Otherwise, the counselor can summarize the session, discuss homework, anticipate difficulties, and confirm the next appointment.

It may be helpful to look at each counseling session like a movie. A good movie typically sets up a situation; creates tension, which eventually reaches a climax; and then resolves to a conclusion. The audience is often given a final few minutes to savor the ending. Counseling sessions should follow a similar pattern, building toward the important work of the hour and then resolving.

Prioritize, Prioritize, Prioritize!

It is important that counselors always keep in mind the urgency of any particular concern. Some problems can be deferred or worked on at a leisurely pace, but if a problem represents a severe safety or health concern, it should be addressed immediately. Thus, as counselors interview a client, they should have an ear out for issues that need to be addressed immediately. So, for example, if a client comes to the session heavily intoxicated, the counselor must address the resulting safety issues. The client should not leave the session alone. His or her spouse or a friend may have to come to pick him or her up. If the client needs detoxification, the counselor can arrange a referral to a detox program. Alternatively, the client may be able to stay on the premises until he or she is sober. Severe depression, extreme anger, suicidal thoughts, or urges to hurt someone are all issues that must be addressed in the session. They are essentially questions of crisis management.

If there are no immediate crises to address, it is still important to prioritize the concerns the client comes in with. The client's priorities may differ from the counselor's. If so, the counselor needs to make a tactical decision about whether to insist on his or her priorities or "give in" to the client's. I suggest that if a counselor has a really good rationale for his or her agenda, he or she can offer it and see whether the client agrees. Sometimes, however, it is not clear that the counselor's goal is more important than the client's, so why not go along with the client?

In the course of the work with a client, counselors will see shifts in priorities, and new issues will arise. They should be noted and prioritized along with the other goals. For instance, a client might become depressed, report drinking signals, become homeless, or start a romantic relationship.

Readings and Resources

Center for Substance Abuse Treatment. (1998). *Therapy manuals for drug abuse: Vol. 1. A cognitive-behavioral approach: Treating cocaine addiction* (NIDA Publication No. 98-4308). Rockville, MD: U.S. Department of Health and Human Services, Public Health Service, National Institutes of Health.

This book includes a good rationale for CBT for treatment of addictive disorders and a good discussion of timing in sessions.

Center for Substance Abuse Treatment. (1999). *Enhancing motivation for change in substance use disorder treatment* (Treatment Improvement Protocol Series 35, DHHS Publication No. SMA 99-3354). Rockville, MD: Substance Abuse and Mental Health Services Administration.

This book includes a good rationale for MI for the treatment of substance use disorders.

Exercises

E.3.1. Rationale for an Intervention

Develop a rationale for an intervention (e.g., psychiatric referral, detoxification, psychiatric medication, specialized treatment for posttraumatic stress disorder, participation in AA or NA) or treatment approach (e.g., methadone maintenance treatment program, therapeutic community, MI, or CBT). Then conduct a team role-play in which each team member gives his or her rationale to a student role-playing a client. This student should react to the rationale. This will be a part of the workbook log. Be sure that the observers keep a detailed record.

E.3.2. Case Study Review

Review case studies for clinical concerns. List them and then prioritize them.

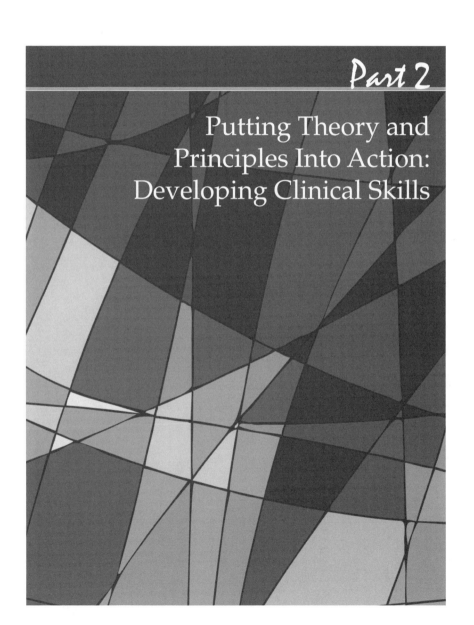

Part 2

Putting Theory and
Principles Into Action:
Developing Clinical Skills

Chapter 4

Applying the Principles of Building Session Goals and Strategies (BSGS) to Prepare for a Session With a Client

This chapter focuses on how to use BSGS principles to organize and focus sessions with clients. You will learn how to determine a specific goal for the session, how to choose techniques to achieve the goal, and how to evaluate whether you were successful. Included in the chapter is an extensive list of techniques you can use, along with their descriptions. At the end of the chapter, I discuss the challenge of being flexible as a counselor while maintaining the goals that you feel are appropriate.

The BSGS principles are as follows:

1. The counselor's first task is to determine what is the most important thing to accomplish in the session he or she is about to conduct.
2. Next, the counselor should determine what strategies and techniques will help achieve this goal.
3. After the session, the counselor evaluates whether the goal was accomplished.

Determining the Most Important Goal for the Session

As you determine the most important goal for the session, the first thing to consider is whether any crises require immediate attention. If a crisis has arisen, you must put all other considerations aside until it is dealt with. (See the Prioritize, Prioritize, Prioritize! section of Chapter 3 for examples of crises.) When the crisis is resolved or if no crisis has occurred, consider the following guidelines for determining the most important goal in the session:

1. The client may indicate the goal directly (e.g., "I have a big problem I have to solve").
2. The client may indicate the goal indirectly. He or she may show distress, anxiety, or another strong emotion or be puzzled. The goal then becomes to clarify the emotion, help the client understand it, and provide guidance.
3. At other times, goals are dictated by behavior that clients avoid talking about, such as noncompliance. In these cases, it is important to be tactful in bringing up the concern.
4. Whenever the client reports a major life change or event, it should be discussed.

Choosing Strategies and Techniques

Once the goal has been determined, think about the strategies and techniques that will help achieve it. *Strategy* refers to interim steps one may take to achieve an overall objective, and in deciding on strategies, the counselor has a chance to be creative. Look at the example in the Ways to Use BSGS in Specific Clinical Scenarios section of this chapter that illustrates how to deal with a relapse. In the example, I suggest a three-step strategy: setting the conditions for the client to talk about the relapse (this conversation could be difficult and embarrassing), determining the meaning of the relapse, and then developing a relapse plan. Rolling with resistance can also be considered a strategy. This is discussed below as well. The following sections list techniques for helping clients achieve their goals.

Anticipate

Often, clients announce a decision that the counselor may feel is ill advised. When this happens, counselors can help clients anticipate potential problems with their decisions rather than disagreeing with them outright.

Break Goals Into Manageable Steps

Clients often feel change is impossible because of the great discrepancy between where they are and where they want to be. If the counselor can break the overarching goal down into smaller, more manageable goals, clients may feel their task is more possible, and when they do achieve each of these smaller goals, they feel more confident that they can change further.

Build Motivation

Many clients are not highly motivated when they first come to counseling. When this is the case, the counselor's job is to help build motivation. (Building motivation is discussed further in Chapter 6.)

Confront

Sometimes clients ignore salient issues, behavior, or feelings. When this happens, the counselor needs to find a constructive way to bring these issues to the client's attention without eliciting defensiveness.

Defuse

Clients can be overwhelmed with emotions, such as anger, depression, and anxiety. The counselor can help defuse these feelings through acceptance, understanding, reassurance, perspective, and humor.

Develop the Relationship or Therapeutic Alliance

An important ingredient in change is building a trusting relationship with clients. When they develop trust in their counselor, they are more likely to be willing to disclose painful experiences and listen to feedback. Research shows the therapeutic alliance to be an important element of treatment (Lambert & Barley, 2002).

Educate

The client may be unaware of or lack knowledge about important concerns. As a general rule, counselors should not take for granted that the client understands specific information until they know the client well.

Offer Empathy

Empathy means that one feels genuine concern for the client's problems. (See Chapters 2 and 5 for a discussion of empathy.)

Assign Homework

Just talking about problems does not cure them. Actions must be planned and carried through. Counselors need to develop action steps clients can take during the time between sessions that will move them closer to their goals. These, of course, should be monitored.

Make Use of Humor

Judicious use of humor can help to defuse painful emotions, provide perspective, and make counseling more enjoyable.

Provide Interpretation and Insight

The meaning of some patterns of behavior may be hidden from the client. When appropriate, it is helpful to point out these meanings.

Listen

Many clients have rarely been listened to. By listening attentively, the counselor shows respect and concern and learns about the clients, and the clients can feel better understood.

Relate Metaphors or Stories

Counseling can include creative aspects. Sometimes the same old dry facts are neither compelling nor interesting to clients. Counselors can tell stories, relate metaphors, or make analogies to enliven sessions.

Monitor

The counselor can keep track of a number of important elements of treatment and bring them up when called for, including attendance, progress, treatment compliance, mood, openness, progress in achieving goals, drug and alcohol use, and homework.

Normalize

Often, clients have experiences in recovery that can be upsetting or frightening. For example, some clients do not function as well in early sobriety as they did when they were drinking. The counselor can explain that this is a common experience for people in recovery, discuss the problem, and reassure the client that it will pass. (In this case, knowledge about substance use disorders is important. Alcohol-dependent clients in early recovery often suffer from temporary cognitive impairment. See Yalisove, 2004, Chapter 3, for a discussion of this temporary impairment.)

Offer Acceptance

Accept clients where they are. Do not judge them or tell them what they must do. Once clients accept their true situation, they can develop the motivation to take steps to change.

Provide Operational Empathy

Operational empathy refers to what the counselor thinks are the logical expectations a person might bring to the counseling situation. (This concept, which I developed, is discussed in Chapter 5.)

Prioritize

Often, clients have multiple problems and no method to sort them out. The counselor can help the client prioritize the issues and develop a plan to systematically begin to change the situation. The treatment plan is the written document that records this process (see Chapter 13 for a discussion of treatment plans).

Problem Solve

If a client has a problem, the counselor can work with him or her to help solve it. They can review the relevant facts, consider the options, and weigh them together.

Promote Openness

Do you notice that in some relationships you hold back feelings, thoughts, and actions, whereas in other relationships, you may feel more open to disclose? Clearly, the latter is better for counseling. Counselors should strive to create a climate in the session that encourages clients to open up.

Provide Advice and Suggestions

Although counseling is not primarily giving advice, some advice can be useful at times, especially when clients ask for it. If the situation seems ripe for advice but the client has not explicitly asked for it, you can ask whether he or she would like some. If the client agrees, you can provide it, using a tentative formulation.

For example, if a client has begun a new romantic relationship and is having difficulty deciding whether to tell the partner about his or her substance use disorder, you can say, "Would you like some advice about this?" If the client assents, you can go on: "In most cases, holding it in causes stress, and it's a relief to get it out; in most cases, the partner is accepting and supportive of the problem. There are a number of ways to tell your partner; have you thought about what you'd like to say? We can review it and see if it's the best approach for you."

Offer Hope

Often, clients feel hopeless. The counselor can be a counterbalance to that despair by expressing hope. Of course, it is important to be realistic rather than Pollyanna-ish.

Provide Reassurance

Counselors can help clients overcome understandable fears and challenges by realistically appraising the clients' capacities and affirming a willingness to stand by them.

Refer

If clients have problems that the counselor lacks the expertise to help solve, he or she must refer them to an appropriate agency or professional. Research shows that counselors' involvement in making the contact with the referral, such as calling and making the appointment with the client present, increases the compliance rate for client follow-through (Bien, Miller, & Tonnigan, 1993).

Reflect

By restating the important things clients say, the counselor demonstrates an effort to understand the issues clients are facing.

Reframe

Clients often see an event in a certain way; the counselor may be able to see the same facts in a different and more constructive light. For example, a client may complain that his wife has been nagging him about his drinking. A counselor can reframe this by saying, "She is concerned about your drinking, but she does not express it in a helpful way" (see W. R. Miller & Rollnick, 1991).

Reward

Too many clients have known nothing but punishment and reprimand. The counselor should look for ways to reward clients for positive behavior. Simply commending a client when he or she has made progress can be very helpful.

Roll With Resistance

When the client is resistant, the counselor needs to avoid getting into a confrontation. He or she should back off and find a way to engage the client constructively. A good analogy for this strategy comes from sailing. When a big storm comes up, sailors take down the ship's sails to keep them from being damaged by the high winds. Although the ship will not make progress during the storm, it will be able to sail when the weather clears. This technique is an essential part of MI.

Self-Disclose

Occasionally a counselor might find that he or she has had a problem similar to something the client is dealing with. In these cases, the counselor may be able to share his or her own experiences and the solution he or she found as a means to connect with clients and help them solve their own problem. Such self-disclosure should only be used to help clients, however. It is not appropriate to burden clients with one's own problems. Research suggests that judicious use of self-disclosure is appreciated by clients and can be helpful (Hill & Knox, 2002).

Give Support

A counselor can give clients the feeling that he or she is there to back them up and to help them through difficult times.

Offer Understanding

Counselors can point out issues that clients are confronted with but are unaware of, such as grief reactions, trauma, neglect, and the reasons for clients' angry outbursts.

Counselors have much to consider in choosing techniques. In general, I recommend that you use the smallest hammer necessary to get the job done In other words, use the least intrusive intervention that can reasonably be expected to achieve the session goal. If that does not work, choose a slightly bigger hammer, and so on. Another way to choose techniques is on the basis of the client's stage of change. See Table 4.1 for some ideas about how to do this.

Evaluating Whether the Goal Was Achieved

Remember, this is the third step in the BSGS process. Asking the client his or her opinion is an important aspect of evaluating goal achievement.

Table 4.1

Appropriate Motivational Strategies for Each Stage of Change

Client's Stage of Change	*Appropriate Motivational Strategies for the Clinician*
Precontemplation: The client is not yet considering change or is unwilling or unable to change.	Establish rapport, ask permission, and build trust. Raise doubts or concerns in the client about substance-using patterns by <ul><li>exploring the meaning of events that brought the client to treatment or the results of previous treatments,</li><li>eliciting the client's perceptions of the problem,</li><li>offering factual information about the risks of substance use,</li><li>providing personalized feedback about assessment findings,</li><li>exploring the pros and cons of substance use,</li><li>helping a significant other intervene, and</li><li>examining the discrepancies between the client's and others' perceptions of the problem behavior.</li></ul> Express concern, and keep the door open.
Contemplation: The client acknowledges concerns and is considering the possibility of change but is ambivalent and uncertain.	Normalize ambivalence. Help the client "tip the decisional balance scales" toward change by <ul><li>eliciting and weighing the pros and cons of substance use and change;</li><li>changing extrinsic to intrinsic motivation;</li><li>examining the client's personal values in relation to change; and</li><li>emphasizing the client's free choice, responsibility, and self-efficacy for change.</li></ul> Elicit self-motivational statements of intent and commitment from the client. Elicit ideas regarding the client's perceived self-efficacy and expectations regarding treatment. Summarize self-motivational statements.
Preparation: The client is committed to making a change in the near future but is still considering what to do.	Clarify the client's own goals and strategies for change. Offer a menu of options for change or treatment. With permission, offer expertise and advice. Negotiate a change—or treatment—plan and behavior contract. Consider and lower barriers to change. Help the client enlist social support. Explore treatment expectancies and the client's role.

(Continued)

Table 4.1 (*Continued*)

Appropriate Motivational Strategies for Each Stage of Change

Client's Stage of Change	Appropriate Motivational Strategies for the Clinician
Preparation: The client is committed to making a change in the near future but is still considering what to do. (*Continued*)	Elicit from the client what has worked in the past either for him or her or for others whom he or she knows.
	Help the client to negotiate finances, child care, work, transportation, or other potential barriers.
	Have the client publicly announce plans to change.
Action: The client is actively taking steps to change but has not yet reached a stable state.	Engage the client in treatment, and reinforce the importance of remaining in recovery.
	Support a realistic view of change through small steps.
Maintenance: The client has achieved initial goals, such as abstinence, and is now working to maintain gains.	Acknowledge difficulties for the client in early stages of change.
	Help the client identify high-risk situations through a functional analysis, and develop appropriate coping strategies to overcome these situations.
	Assist the client in finding new reinforcers of positive change.
	Help the client assess whether he or she has strong family and social support.
	Help the client identify and sample drug-free sources of pleasure (i.e., new reinforcers).
	Support lifestyle changes.
	Affirm the client's resolve and self-efficacy.
	Help the client practice and use new coping strategies to avoid a return to use.
	Maintain a supportive contact (e.g., explain to the client that you are available to talk between sessions).
	Develop a "fire escape" plan to implement if the client resumes substance use.
	Review long-term goals with the client.
Recurrence: The client has experienced a recurrence of symptoms and must now cope with the consequences and decide what to do next.	Help the client reenter the change cycle, and commend any willingness to reconsider positive change.
	Explore the meaning and reality of the recurrence as a learning opportunity.
	Assist the client in finding alternative coping strategies.
	Maintain supportive contact.

Note. Adapted from *Enhancing Motivation for Change in Substance Use Disorder Treatment* (Treatment Improvement Protocol Series 35, DHHS Publication No. SMA 99-3354), by the Center for Substance Abuse Treatment, 1999, Rockville, MD: Substance Abuse and Mental Health Services Administration.

Counseling is a collaborative process, and one of its goals is for the counselor and client to be working cooperatively together. So at the end of the session, the counselor might ask, "Do you feel we made progress today in [cite the specific issue—e.g., "understanding your relapse"]?"

Another, equally important aspect is objectively measuring the client's progress. A number of goals can be measured objectively. For example, abstinence can be demonstrated with drug-free urine specimens. Participation in self-help can be measured by the number of self-help meetings the client attended in the month.

A third source of information is the counselor's reactions during and immediately after the session. If you feel positive, try to determine what about the session led to this feeling. If you have feelings of confusion, irritation, annoyance, or disappointment, try to figure out what happened in the session to create these feelings, so that you can improve your approach in subsequent sessions.

Ways to Use BSGS in Specific Clinical Scenarios

Now let's look at some specific scenarios and develop BSGS goals and techniques for them. In the first example, the client is resistant. Resistance occurs when a client is not cooperating, not complying with treatment requirements, or not listening to the counselor. The goal is to reduce resistance.

The goal of this example may sound obvious, but it is important. When counselors focus on reducing resistance, they must stop action in other areas until the resistance is reduced (Center for Substance Abuse Treatment, 1999, pp. 46–49). One cannot try to convince the client he or she is a drug addict, must have treatment, and is in denial. Such an approach is like "piling on" in football; it muddies the water. Resistance calls for efforts to reduce it. It is a sign that the counselor and the client are not on the same page. The goal, therefore, is to get on the same page so that cooperation can resume.

To reduce resistance, the counselor can choose from several techniques. He or she can opt to roll with the resistance or problem solve the impasse with the client. Sometimes a temporary retreat is a good strategy. For example, in a military contest, retreating to a better defended area may provide enough advantage to ensure a victory. In the 1974 world heavyweight boxing championship, Muhammad Ali used the rope-a-dope strategy to tire out his opponent, George Foreman, and win the match. He took a defensive approach for several rounds, absorbing all of Foreman's punches, leaning on the ropes while his opponent expended all of his energy in the early rounds. At the end of the bout, Foreman was hardly able to keep his hands up, and Ali knocked him out in the eighth round. Similarly, counselors may find it effective to wait out a client's resistance, following the client's lead until he or she is more open to change.

Alternatively, a counselor may be working with a patient who has relapsed. In this case, the goal is to restore remission (patients in remission no longer have any of the symptoms of substance abuse or dependence). For most substance abuse clients, remission means becoming abstinent again. For some clients with a substance abuse diagnosis, remission may mean that their use of alcohol or other drugs is not harmful or dangerous (e.g., controlled drinking). This goal may also sound obvious, but counselors actually need to take three steps to facilitate this goal. First, they need to create an atmosphere in which the client can talk freely about the relapse. Second, they need to determine the meaning of the relapse to the client and build his or her motivation to restore remission. Third, if the client is motivated to restore remission, an abstinence plan can be developed.

With a client who has relapsed, the first goal is to engage the client and discuss the relapse nonjudgmentally. The counselor can do this by accepting the client, normalizing the situation, and being empathic. These techniques promote an open discussion of the relapse.

Once the client is open to discussing the relapse, the counselor's next goal is to use the conversation to learn what the relapse reveals about the client's motivation, skills, environment, and other relevant factors. The counselor can use this information to build the client's motivation to restore remission. Exploring the client's feelings about the relapse, discussing the events that preceded the relapse, and determining the client's commitment and ability to become abstinent are effective techniques for accomplishing this goal.

Finally, the counselor's third goal is to develop an abstinence plan with the client. He or she can do this by problem solving with the client and anticipating any roadblocks to abstinence that the client may encounter, then making a plan with the client to overcome them.

Let's look at how we could evaluate goal achievement in the above two examples, reducing resistance and restoring remission. Whether resistance has been reduced is easily determined in the session by the client's actions. A counselor can see that resistance is reduced when the client stops interrupting, ignoring, arguing, or disagreeing and begins to agree and cooperate. With a client who has had a relapse, remission can be measured by the client's self-report of abstinence and by clean urine specimens and breathalyzer readings. Other positive actions the client takes are also relevant, such as attending self-help meetings.

Treatment Integrity Versus Flexibility

One of the fundamental challenges in becoming a good counselor is determining the balance between adherence to treatment principles and flexibility in revising approaches to suit the specific client and clinical situation. On the one hand, counselors should be knowledgeable about the techniques of counseling and skillful in applying them. They should adhere to the principles of the approach they espouse. If counselors claim to be using the CBT approach to substance abuse, they should, in fact, be using techniques derived from that approach. This is called *treatment integrity*. Researchers have developed treatment manuals in part to specify what the counselor should be doing to be faithful to the kind of treatment that is being given. Supervision, videotaping of sessions, and other forms of observation can then used to measure how well the counselor is following the manual. The format of your role-play logs will give you an opportunity to measure your adherence to the goals and techniques you developed for your role-play.

On the other hand, specific clinical situations may require a good deal of modification to the protocol provided by the treatment manual. Even the most detailed manuals cannot account for all the unexpected events that may arise in treatment situations. For that reason, most treatment manuals suggest that counselors use flexibility and judgment in determining whether to adhere to the plan or make some modification.

Similarly, although BSGS stresses an active, prepared stance in sessions, it is also important to be flexible. A counselor should prepare goals and techniques for his or her sessions, but changes in the client's situation may require the counselor to change those goals and techniques. For example, let's say your client is not yet committed to becoming abstinent, and you have planned to build motivation by using the decisional balance (evaluating the pros and cons of continuing to use and stopping). When the client comes to a session heavily intoxicated, however, clearly you must revise the goal of the session to consider a referral for detoxification to ensure the client's safety and health. Rarely do sessions go as planned. Therefore, counselors need to develop flexibility while maintaining a good sense of where the counseling needs to go. Hubble et al. (1999) pointed out that flexibility helps counselors maintain a good therapeutic relationship with their clients.

Readings and Resources

Center for Substance Abuse Treatment. (2000). *A cognitive–behavioral approach: Treating cocaine addiction* (NIDA NIH Publication No. 00-4308). Bethesda, MD: U.S. Department of Health and Human Services, National Institutes of Health, National Institute on Drug Abuse.
This is a good example of a treatment manual.

Center for Substance Abuse Treatment. (2000). *A community reinforcement plus vouchers approach: Treating cocaine addiction* (NIDA NIH Publication No. 00-4309). Bethesda, MD: U.S. Department of Health and Human Services, National Institutes of Health, National Institute on Drug Abuse.
This is another good example of a treatment manual.

Exercises

E.4.1. Interactions With People

Think about the people you interact with. Think of the one person you hold back most from and the person you disclose the most to. Now think about the reasons why you interact differently with these two people. How is this relevant to your counseling approach? This will be a part of the workbook log.

E.4.2. Session Goals and Techniques

Develop a goal and techniques for the following scenarios:

a. The patient is resistant to attending AA or NA.
b. The client becomes depressed.
c. The client reports "drink signals" (i.e., the client is afraid he or she might drink).
d. The client becomes homeless.
e. The client starts a romantic relationship.
f. The client wants to leave treatment prematurely and try to change on his or her own.
g. The client is noncompliant (e.g., misses sessions, is chronically late, or does not do homework).

This will be a part of the workbook log.

E.4.3. Measuring Goals

What are some ways of objectively measuring the goals you developed for the scenarios in E.4.2 by the end of the session and over a period of time? List additional goals and how they can be measured. This will be useful when we take up treatment plans in Chapter 13. This will be a part of the workbook log.

E.4.4. Role-Play: Intoxicated Client

Role-play a scenario with an intoxicated client. One team member plays the role of the counselor, and another plays the client. Determine the goal of the session and the techniques the counselor will use before beginning the role-play. Be sure that the observers keep a detailed record of the dialogue. This will be a part of the workbook log.

E.4.5. Role-Play: Resistant Client

In a team role-play, role-play a resistant client and a counselor who rolls with the resistance. Choose any combination of the following client traits: antagonistic, argumentative, defensive, oppositional, rude, in denial of any substance use problems, and so on; choose a substance use disorder case study that fits. (A good source for cases is Kelly & Juhnke's, 2005, casebook of clients with addictive disorders.) This exercise is simply intended to help you learn to use the technique, and the technique is just one of the tools that you will learn to use. This exercise will be a part of the workbook log. Be sure that the observer keeps a detailed record. The goal of this session is to roll with resistance, and the technique is to roll with resistance. Underline and label client resistance in the verbatim record, as well as instances when the counselor rolled with resistance. Note the client's reaction when this occurs.

Extra Credit Projects

4.a. Skills to practice with a partner. Just see whether you can perform each of the following techniques in a role-play:

- reflection,
- giving advice, and
- reframing.

4.b. Do you know any stories or metaphors that might be helpful in the counseling situation? Write them down, and discuss how they might be helpful in counseling.

Chapter 5

Building Session Goals and Strategies (BSGS) and the First Session

In this chapter, the focus is on how to apply the principles of BSGS to the first session. Appropriate session goals and strategies are discussed, and the concepts of empathy, operational empathy, and reflection are introduced. First, let's apply the BSGS principles laid out in Chapter 2 to develop the appropriate goals and techniques for clients coming in for their first session. The three steps are as follows:

1. to determine what is the most important thing to accomplish in the session you are about to conduct;
2. to determine what strategies and techniques will help achieve this goal; and
3. to evaluate, after the session, whether you accomplished the goal.

Developing Goals for the First Session

For the purposes of this example, let's assume the client is not having a crisis that needs to be addressed. (If the client does come to the first session in crisis, obviously the major goal for that session is to resolve the crisis.) Ideally, by the end of the first session the counselor has oriented the client to the purpose of the session, screened for admission, begun to get the client's story, defined the problems that need to be solved in counseling, begun building rapport, and provided encouragement and support. Often, the counselor cannot complete all of these goals. The most important goal in the first session, if the counselor feels the client has a substance use disorder, is to get the client to come back! First-session goals and the respective techniques that can help achieve each goal are listed in Table 5.1. Let's discuss the goals and techniques one by one.

Goal 1: Orient the Client to the Purpose and Method of the First Session

At the beginning of the first session, the counselor needs to orient the client to the process. At a minimum, the counselor might say, "We're going to meet for 45 minutes; we can discuss the concerns you have and see if I can be of help. What you tell me will be confidential unless you tell me something that is a threat to yourself or someone else. I will discuss my findings with the treatment team to determine the best treatment for you."

The mention of confidentiality includes disclosure that in some limited instances, the counselor is required to report information. During the session, explain all of the tasks that you do or talk about. Answer all of the questions the client asks regarding the procedures. Be sure the client understands the process.

Table 5.1
Goals and Techniques for the First Session

Session Goal	Technique
1. Orient client to the purpose and method of the first session.	Education to help the client understand the treatment process
2. Screen for admission. Is the client in the right place for his or her current needs?	Screening test, such as AUDIT to make a preliminary assessment of alcohol problems and DAST for drugs. Open-ended questions to obtain details about drug and alcohol use
3. Begin to get the client to tell his or her story	Open-ended questions to elicit the client's story Listen
4. Define the problem to be solved	A combination of reflection, summary, and sometimes reframing
5. Build rapport	Empathy and operational empathy to promote rapport Reflection to show empathy, and listening to demonstrate interest and concern
6. Provide motivation for continuing the counseling process	Provide encouragement, support, and praise for attending the session to begin to address the problems at hand

Note. AUDIT = Alcohol Use Disorders Identification Test; DAST = Drug Abuse Screening Test.

Goal 2: Screen for Admission

In addition to determining whether the current program seems appropriate for the client's needs, discuss briefly other practical matters, such as the cost of the program and insurance coverage.

Goal 3: Begin to Get the Client to Tell His or Her Story

An important objective of the first session is to understand the problem that needs to be solved. The best way to achieve this is to have the client tell the full story about what is troubling him or her. It is not necessary to focus on substance use at this time; it will be addressed by the end of the session. Some clients are eager to have the opportunity to "spill," and all they need is an open-ended question: "What brings you here today?" An *open-ended* question is one the client cannot answer with just a few words. It is an invitation for the client to tell his or her story. A *closed-ended* question asks for a simple, discrete answer, such as "yes" or "no," and thus discourages the client from elaborating his or her story.

Some clients are reserved or ambivalent about sharing aspects of their personal life with a stranger. Those who are reluctant need reassurance that the counselor will be a sympathetic listener, helpful, and nonjudgmental. With such clients, the approach of Carl Rogers (1965), creator of client-centered therapy, is most helpful. Rogers (1965) suggested that genuineness and empathy are the key elements in gaining the client's trust so he or she will be willing to open up. That is, if the counselor is genuinely interested in the client and can show it, the client will begin to open up. The demonstration of empathy flows from a genuine feeling of interest and concern.

Empathy is a key concept in counseling and psychotherapy. It refers to the capacity to understand and feel for the client respectfully. It does not mean getting drawn into the client's feelings, nor does it mean agreeing with everything he or she says. A term I created, *operational empathy*, may give you a basic understanding of empathy. When you go to the doctor, you have certain expectations about the visit. You expect the doctor to be knowledgeable, tell you his or her assessment of your condition and any diagnoses, explain what the treatments are, and maintain a professional and respectful attitude. You may be anxious because you are awaiting the results of a biopsy or other test. It is important for the doctor to remain within your reasonable expectations. For example, you expect to immediately be given the results of the tests, their meaning, and options for treatment if indicated. If the doctor delays telling you, tells you a joke, or talks about his or her bad day, this will make you anxious or angry.

Similarly, clients who come to substance abuse counseling have expectations. Because counseling is less clearly defined than a doctor's visit, there is a greater chance for misapprehension on the client's part. As a first step toward understanding empathy, it is worthwhile to consider what a reasonable client would expect to transpire in a counseling session.

Whenever we must go outside what is reasonably to be expected, we need to explain to the client why we are doing so (i.e., provide a rationale). So, for example, if the client came to counseling for relief of depression but the counselor determines that the client's drug use is dangerously out of control and feels the client needs to be evaluated for inpatient admission for detoxification and severe depression, the counselor must carefully explain why he or she is suggesting this treatment.

Empathy is an important technique because it facilitates the client's ability to tell his or her story openly. In the beginning of therapy, a vital goal is learning about the client's world (getting to know the lay of the land). A basic postulate is that if one learns enough about the client's world, one will know what to say and how to help him or her. If one is not so clear, one is shooting in the dark, so to speak.

Reflection is a client-centered technique counselors use to determine whether they understand what the client is expressing. The counselor restates the essence of what he or she feels the client has said. Reflecting doesn't mean echoing or parroting. Rather, use reflection strategically. When you reflect, you are underlining what you think is important about what the client is saying. Good reflections are a way of showing empathy. For example, if a client becomes sad and tearful when he discusses how much he has alienated his family over his drinking, the counselor might say, "Your family is very important to you, and you are concerned that your drinking has hurt them" (reflecting the essence of the client's words).

In this example, the reflection focuses on the client's concern about his family as a potential motivating force to address his drinking problem. Thus, the reflection serves the double function of demonstrating empathy by showing that the counselor is listening and, at the same time, developing motivation. Sometimes empathy is not enough to enable the client to tell his or her story. If this happens, I offer some suggestions at the end of the chapter to help draw the client out.

If alcohol and drugs are prominently featured in the client's story, he or she is a candidate for substance abuse treatment. If the client makes no reference to alcohol or drugs, you can point out that he or she has come to a substance abuse clinic, so you need to see whether drugs or alcohol are contributing to his or her problems. You can also administer a screening instrument, such as the AUDIT (Babor et al., 2001) or the Drug Abuse Screening Test (DAST-20; Skinner, 1982) to determine whether the client has a substance abuse or alcohol problem. (These tests are reprinted in Appendix C.)

Goal 4: Define the Problem to Be Solved

One approach is to provide a diagnosis and your expertise about the problem. What are the downsides to this method? The approach I advocate is to summarize the client's concerns and begin to problem solve and offer a list of possible approaches, as expressed in the following example:

Counselor: It seems that you have some concerns about your drinking but you're not certain what you want to do about it. One of your concerns is that it is affecting your relationship with your family, and that's important to you. Some people with a dilemma like this gain some perspective talking about it. Another thing we might do is get some detailed information about your drinking pattern and its consequences. This involves taking standardized tests. This may help you decide what you want to do. What do you think?

Client: It might help, and it probably won't hurt.

Counselor: Good. This is a positive step for you.

Sometimes you may have sufficient information to define a problem, but you and the client are not seeing eye to eye on the goals. Try negotiating goals with the client. For example, if the client clearly is alcohol dependent, drinks heavily, and refuses to consider detoxification in the hospital after you have given the recommendation and rationale for the hospitalization and expressed concern for the client's safety and health, suggest outpatient medically supervised detoxification. If the client resists that, discuss how he or she has detoxified in the past and whether that method worked, and suggest that he or she stay with a reliable relative or friend for the period of withdrawal and call you daily. This roadblock of goal differences between counselor and client can occur anytime during treatment. If it arises in the first session, it is more important to get the client to come back than to insist that your goal is the right one.

Goal 5: Build Rapport

You can build rapport by being respectful, being warm but professional, and demonstrating empathy and concern for the client. Answer the client's questions as best you can. Be sympathetic to his or her concerns. Listen.

Goal 6: Provide Motivation for Continuing the Counseling Process

Compliment the client for coming and sharing his or her concerns. Provide a realistic sense of hope that the client will overcome his or her problems. Discuss, in a general sense, some of the kinds of help the client can get. Motivation at this point is more geared to getting the client involved in counseling than to committing him or her to stopping the use of drugs or alcohol. Of course, if the client has a strong motivation for abstinence, the counselor can reinforce it.

Wrap-Up

If you complete all of the goals listed for the first session, toward the end of the session you should do the following:

- Summarize the session.
- Suggest a plan: What will the client do between now and the next session that will help him or her move toward the goals of treatment?
- Discuss any homework or goals that the client has agreed to.
- Anticipate problems in the coming week.
- Ask the client whether he or she has any questions.
- Set a specific appointment time for the next session.

Sometimes the counselor cannot accomplish all of his or her goals for a session. This is where flexibility comes in. If you are not finished with all of the goals and see you are not going to finish, summarize what you and the client did together, suggest that you continue next time, and schedule another appointment to do so.

Evaluate the Outcome of the Session

The third step of BSGS is to evaluate the session and self-reflect about what happened. Were the goals appropriate? Were the techniques appropriate? What could be improved? For example, if the client asked for clarification a number of times about something you said, think about how you might better explain the issue the next time it comes up.

Roadblock: The Client Is Not Freely Telling His or Her Story

Suppose the client is not freely telling his or her story. You cannot determine the problem that needs to be solved, and you are not getting the lay of the land. In this case, the goal is obvious: Get the client to tell his or her story.

The following techniques can help overcome this roadblock:

1. Reflect the problem by saying, for example, "It's not easy for you to talk about your problems today."
2. Explain that you cannot do your job to help if you do not have a good picture of the problem and the lay of the land. For example, you could say, "The way counseling works is for us to get a good picture of your life and current problems and then develop a set of goals to work on. So it's important to get a clear idea of these things so we find the right goals for you."
3. Elicit the client's concerns about opening up. For example, say, "It may be hard for you to open up to a stranger. Do you have some concerns about it? Are you concerned about who will know about what you tell me?"
4. Ask about possible distractors: drug use; intoxication; withdrawal from drugs; a crisis hanging over the client; or strong emotional reactions, such as anger or depression. For example, ask, "Is there something going on that may make it difficult to talk today?"

5. Ask what would help the client to open up.
6. Start with little problems in the client's life to prime the pump (e.g., "What were some of the little problems you had today? This week?").
7. Use your observations to see whether you can intuit the problem. The client may seem depressed, angry, or withdrawn or show signs of other emotions. If the client is not talking about these feelings, you can suggest that they may be the problem to be solved. For example, you could say, "You seem to be sad today; is that one of the problems you would like to work on?"

Whatever approach you use, be patient with the client.

Exercises

E.5.1. Opening Statement

a. Compose your opening statement for a new client.
b. Role-play this opening statement with your partner. He or she should react to it. Be sure that the observers keep a detailed record. This will be a part of the workbook log.

E.5.2. Creating Rapport

Recall situations in your life in which physicians and other professionals were good at creating rapport and not so good at this. How are these experiences relevant to your counseling approach? This will be a part of the workbook log.

E.5.3. Client Expectations

What do you think a client coming to a substance abuse counseling center expects on the first visit? Take a few minutes to consider this; put yourself in the shoes of a client coming to a counseling session for the first time. What would a reasonable client anticipate? What might he or she expect from a first visit to a substance abuse counselor? Write down your reactions. This will be a part of the workbook log.

E.5.4. AUDIT Review and Role-Play

a. Review the AUDIT manual (Babor et al., 2001). Learn how to administer and score the test. The AUDIT manual can be obtained at http://whqlibdoc.who.int/hq/2001/WHO_MSD_MSB_01.6a.pdf.
b. Role-play: Administer the AUDIT (Babor et al., 2001) and give feedback. (See Center for Substance Abuse Treatment, 1999, pp. 65–71, for suggestions on how to give feedback in MI style.) Before doing so, be clear about your goals. What are they? What techniques will

you use? Role-play this exercise with your partner. He or she should react to your feedback. This will be a part of the workbook log. Be sure that the observer keeps a detailed record. When doing the role-play, give the client the following rationale for using the AUDIT modified for use in a substance abuse clinic:

> I am going to ask you some questions about your use of alcohol during the past year. To determine whether you need treatment for alcoholism and, if so, what kind of treatment, it is important for us to know how much you usually drink and whether you have experienced any problems with your drinking. Please try to be as honest and as accurate as you can be.

E.5.5. The "Expert" Approach

Write out an "expert" approach, and try it out on your partner, role-playing any of the case studies. An expert tone sounds like, for example, "From the information I have, it is clear that you are opiate dependent. You need detoxification and then inpatient therapeutic community. This is what is best for you." How does the client feel when this approach is taken? This will be a part of the workbook log. Be sure that the observers keep a detailed record.

E.5.6. Construct a Summary

Use case studies, such as those given in Kelly and Juhnke (2005), to construct a summary of the client's problems in his or her language. Your goal is to define the problem in language the client can relate to.

E.5.7. Open and Closed Questions

Which of the following are open questions and closed questions?

a. Is this a closed question?
b. Is this an open question?
c. How does marijuana fit into your daily life?
d. Are you happy with your use of cocaine?
e. What brings you here today?
f. How much alcohol do you typically drink every day?

Chapter 6

Beyond the First Session:
The Beginning Phase of Treatment

After the introductory session, the focus of counseling is on the process of starting to help the client. The first phase of counseling includes a "getting to know you" aspect, while the counselor evaluates the client's motivation to change and builds that motivation. This chapter also includes a discussion of two important issues in substance abuse treatment: keeping track of the client's drug use, and considerations in treating mandated clients.

Once the client has been admitted to the program, he or she is assigned to a primary counselor, who coordinates the client's treatment and provides individual and, often, group counseling. The first phase of treatment involves rapport building, more education, and development of the agreed-on goals. Crucial to the latter objective is evaluating the client's motivation to change. Many clients enter treatment in the precontemplation or contemplation phase, so building motivation is often the first goal in substance abuse treatment.

The "Getting to Know You" Aspect of Treatment

Clients in counseling are expected to talk about some very personal things. Sometimes it is difficult for them to talk about their problems with self-control, their debts, their failures in relationships, their inability to cut down on drugs or alcohol, and even more traumatic events, such as childhood sexual abuse. Part of what the counselor should do in the early sessions is create an atmosphere in which the client can feel at ease and open up. To this end, the principles of client-centered therapy (Rogers, 1965) make a lot of sense. The discussion of empathy and genuineness in Chapter 5 remains relevant here. Showing interest in the client's life also helps. You must balance this aspect of your role with certain other tasks that you need to perform as well. You must explain the rules of the clinic and make sure the client follows them. For example, you need to explain the random urinalysis policy (this is discussed later in the chapter) and begin to help the client see the role of drugs and alcohol in his or her problems.

Evaluating the Client's Motivation to Change

Before a counselor presents treatment goals and options to clients, it is important to assess clients' motivation. If I go to a flute teacher and say I want to learn to play the flute, it is probably a good idea for the teacher to explore my motivation. Before the flute teacher assigns me 3 hours of practice a day, recommends sight-reading classes, and requires me to take a course in music theory, it would be a good idea for him or her to assess how important flute playing is to me and how proficient I would like to become. This question of motivation is a central issue in MI, and the stages of change concept goes hand in hand with assessing motivation. One way to evaluate motivation is to administer relevant tests (see Center for Substance Abuse Treatment, 1999, for several examples). It is actually fairly easy, however, to determine the client's state of change and level of motivation by listening carefully to him or her. If the client is in the determination or action stage, the counselor can move on to developing a treatment plan. If not, building motivation becomes the goal.

From the Stages of Change perspective, counselors build motivation by moving the client from his or her current stage to the next one. Thus, if a client is in precontemplation, the counselor's goal is to help him or her move to contemplation. If a client is in contemplation, the goal is to help him or her move to determination, and so on until he or she reaches maintenance. The following is an example of a first session with a client in precontemplation:

Client: I'm only here because I have to be here.
Counselor: What forced you to come?
Client: My boss gave me a random urine test on a Monday morning, and it turned up positive for marijuana. He said I had to come here for an evaluation.
Counselor: So you're here because your job might be on the line.
Client: Yeah. And it's not fair at all. I use a little weed on the weekends. That's none of his business.
Counselor: So you really feel intruded on.
Client: So just write my boss a letter and tell him I was here so he'll get off my back.
Counselor: I would be happy to document your visit here. But I believe he said he wanted an evaluation? What do you think he means by that?

Client: Maybe he thinks I'm a drug addict. That's ridiculous.

Counselor: That's a hard thing to disprove once someone has that suspicion.

Client: Yeah, it's not fair. What can I do? Can you help?

Counselor: Well, maybe if we do a complete evaluation, that would help resolve the issue. We can provide that.

Client: What's involved?

The counselor in this example is trying to move the client toward contemplation. His approach is to first build the client's motivation to participate willingly in an evaluation of his drug and alcohol use. If the counselor can get accurate information and, in fact, the client does show problematic use of substances, then the counselor can tactfully begin to show the client his problems with substance use.

Building Motivation

Clients, like most of us, do not find it easy to acknowledge negative behaviors. Many clients have avoided looking at the negative aspects of their drug use. Therefore, part of building motivation is helping clients develop an awareness of the negative aspects of their drug use without arousing resistance. If the counselor just points out the disadvantages of drug use, the client is likely to become resistant. MI offers a number of tools to raise the client's awareness without eliciting defensiveness; these are discussed in the following sections.

Building Discrepancy

By discussing what is important to the client and seeing how drug use is interfering with these values, counselors can build discrepancy. For example, a client may highly value his or her appearance; the counselor can explore the effects of the client's substance use on his or her appearance even though health issues may be of more concern to the counselor.

Providing Personalized Feedback

By providing the client with objective information about his or her drug use and its effects, the counselor can constructively confront the client with his or her difficulties with drugs and alcohol. One way to provide such information is to administer the AUDIT (Babor et al., 2001) and give feedback about the results. The manner in which the counselor delivers this information is crucial. It is important not to evoke resistance or defensiveness.

Using the Decisional Balance

To use the decisional balance to help motivate a client, the counselor can make a diagram that shows the client's views of the pros and cons of drug use and the pros and cons of stopping. It is best to ask the client to give the pros and cons. The diagram can then be used as a basis for discussing the pros and cons of using and stopping. It can also be placed in the client's medical record, and a copy can be given to the client.

Raising Ambivalence

Strictly speaking, raising ambivalence is not an MI technique, but I believe it fits the spirit of MI. When a counselor points out the ambivalence the client feels about drug use rather than the negative effects drugs are having, the client has a better chance to own the need to change and is less likely to become defensive. The idea is that ambivalence is an unpleasant state. If ambivalence about drug or alcohol use becomes high, the client will be motivated to reduce this painful feeling, as illustrated in the following example of a client musing on his ambivalence:

> *Client:* This is driving me crazy. I can't decide what to do about my marijuana use.
> *Counselor:* This going back and forth is very confusing and upsetting to you.
> *Client:* You know, I could really save myself a lot of pain if I just decided to quit.

Building motivation includes helping the client see that change is possible. This is called *promoting self-efficacy.* The goal is to bolster the client's feeling that he or she can change. If the client is low in self-efficacy, one strategy is to develop small goals that the client can complete and that, when completed, can help build confidence.

Urinalysis and Keeping Track of Drug Use

An obvious and important goal of substance abuse treatment is reduced drug use or abstinence. Thus, it is important to keep track of the client's progress in keeping clean or controlling use. Yet once it has been reviewed in a session, the issue often can and should go into the background. Although it is important to discuss abstinence, it is important not to beat the question to death. I believe in the "just enough" approach: Abstinence must be discussed, but often this discussion may simply mean determining the length of abstinence the client has achieved. In this manner, the counselor can communicate in a nonjudgmental way that substance use is an important issue in the treatment. If the counselor focuses too heavily on the topic, he or she may turn off the client.

I have made a routine practice of inquiring of all my clients at the beginning of the session how long they have been clean. I believe the key is not only what you say but how you say it. If a counselor gives the impression that he or she is expecting a relapse, trying to catch the client lying, or otherwise not trusting the client, this will engender antagonism. So the tone I try to convey is one of routine. That way, I don't make the client feel bad if he or she has relapsed, nor do I give the impression that I expect him or her to relapse. I try to keep the tone light and neutral, in the same manner I would use to ask whether a person slept well the previous night. I might ask something like, "So when did you use drugs last?" If the client has been continuously abstinent since the last known relapse, I say, "Good work," and move on. If he or she acknowledges a lapse or is struggling with urges to use, of course that becomes an important issue to deal with.

Most substance abuse clinics require clients to submit urine samples randomly for toxicology screening. Clinics have procedures for collecting samples that minimize the possibility that clients will provide urine that is adulterated or not their own. Clinics also have policies about the consequences of positive urine tests. Usually, clients are not penalized for a single positive urine test, but if a client does not show a trend of decreased drug use over time, he or she may be discharged. How the counselor presents this requirement can make a big difference in a client's acceptance of and participation in drug testing. Emphasize the positive rather than the negative. For example, point out that clean urine specimens and clean breathalyzers offer objective proof that the client is doing well in dealing with his or her drug problem. Significant others, employers, and other interested parties can appreciate this, so a series of clean urine specimens can begin to restore trust with important people in the client's life.

When a positive urine sample is discovered, it is important to discuss it, but not punitively. You can ask how the client feels about the use and whether the client can stop on his or her own. You can problem solve to help the client deal with triggers to use. (See also the discussion in the Relapse, Recurrence, and Recycling section of Chapter 2 about addressing relapse with clients and the distinction between interrupted use and relapse, as well as the example in Chapter 4 of restoring remission. Relapse prevention is further discussed in Chapter 7.)

Coerced and Mandated Clients

Only a small proportion of substance abuse clients enter treatment voluntarily (Burke & Gregoire, 2007). Obviously, then, most clients are forced or feel forced into treatment to a greater or lesser extent. The nature and degree of the pressure vary. Clients may come to treatment because of concern expressed by a loved one, as a condition of continued employment, or as a condition arising from a criminal justice determination. It may be surprising, but clients coerced into treatment do as well as clients who voluntarily come to treatment (Yalisove, 2004). Thus, it is important not to make assumptions about the motivation of coerced clients. Nor should they be treated as second-class citizens. Still, many coerced clients feel resentful when they begin treatment. If that is the case, it makes sense to build the relationship by seeking to understand and accept the client's feelings. In addition, it is important to be clear about any agreements between the referring agency and the clinic regarding exchange of information and the consequences of the client's behavior—in other words, what the counselor will do if the client does not attend sessions or tests positive for drugs or alcohol, and what the counselor will communicate to the referring agency. It is important to state these conditions clearly and up front in a matter-of-fact way. If the client cannot accept the conditions, he or she can choose to decline the treatment and face the resulting consequences.

Here are some guidelines to help you work with coerced clients:

- Don't make assumptions about coerced clients' motivation or chance to recover.
- Don't treat them as second-class citizens.
- Be clear about any agreements between you and the source of coercion. Review them completely with the client.
- Be sure to learn about all possible sources of coercion and all of their elements.
- Be sure to monitor drug and alcohol use and other aspects of compliance and report them to the appropriate agency, provided that you have a signed release for this purpose.
- Collaborate with the criminal justice professionals or Employee Assistance Program counselors who have responsibility for your clients.

Some additional guidelines may help you work with clients mandated to treatment by the criminal justice system:

- State clearly your role for the client, and establish clear boundaries. Don't make promises you can't keep. Clarify that treatment is not punishment. Don't extend beyond your competence or your appropriate professional role.
- State sanctions for relapses; these should be structured on a graduated scale. One relapse after a long period of abstinence should not be viewed as a failure.
- Determine whether the client displays "criminal thinking" (e.g., believes that his or her criminal activity is justified). Specialized cognitive skills training may help clients overcome this pattern of thinking.
- If the client has children, you can help build the treatment alliance by providing parenting guidance as well as offering some measure of support for the children.
- Problem solve with the client regarding practical matters, such as housing and employment. This will help build a therapeutic relationship.
- If your agency provides services to a large number of clients from the criminal justice system, it is important to learn the processes involved in the local courts, other aspects of the criminal justice system, and how they influence the treatment provided (Center for Substance Abuse Treatment, 2005b).

Some mandated clients may come to treatment intending to find a way to overcome the pending legal matter without addressing their substance use disorder. They may give lip service to abstinence, saying what they think the counselor wants to hear, but their actions and underlying attitude suggest that they are trying to maintain the same basic lifestyle that got them into trouble. In the language of the Stages of Change Model, these clients are in precontemplation. First, counselors should not be surprised by this strategy. It is a pretty sensible approach, from the client's point of view. Second, counselors should not be morally indignant about it.

Still, it is not easy to constructively engage such clients. In the beginning phase of treatment, counselors need to be empathic and helpful in practical matters without being manipulated by the client. They should lend assistance but be careful to clarify what the treatment involves and, when necessary, reframe what the client says. The following imagined dialogue between a counselor and such a client illustrates this balance:

Client: It's really not fair. My parole officer has it in for me. Why do I have to come to treatment? I sold some weed. I don't need it. I just smoke occasionally. Can you just tell him that? That would really help me. I want to get on with my life.

Counselor: You feel he's been unfair. I wonder what led him to make the referral?

Client: Isn't it obvious? I'm Black, and he's White.

Counselor: You feel he's discriminating against you.

Client: What else could it be? He probably thinks all Blacks are drug addicts.

Counselor: I'm not sure. Maybe there are some other reasons. What do you think?

Client: Man, you're just on his side.

Counselor: I don't think so. I haven't spoken to him yet. I try to keep an open mind about things. Parole and treatment are different. My job is to help you if you have a drug problem. We don't really have enough information to know that yet. That would be the first step here, if you'd like to get involved.

Client: How do I know you're not on his side?

Counselor: That will take time. Little by little, you can begin to figure that out. One part of my job is to answer any questions you have about treatment and how I relate to your parole officer. According to our agreement, I am to report regularly to him about your attendance and results of drug and alcohol tests. Do you have any questions about it?

Client: Are you going to tell him I'm a drug addict?

Counselor: Of course not. I don't know whether you have a drug problem.

Client: What will you tell him?

Counselor: I will tell him that you came on time to your first session and
asked some good questions.
Client: Really?
Counselor: Really.

In this example, the counselor acknowledges the client's concerns but
does not get drawn into them. He begins to explain how treatment is different from the criminal justice system. He realizes that it will take a good
deal of time for the client to trust him and knows he may have to prove
himself to the client. By stating that he will tell the probation officer that
the client came to the session on time and asked good questions, he is
communicating to the client that the information he shares with the officer
will be appropriate and nonjudgmental.

This chapter considers the beginning phase of treatment. The objectives
of this phase are to engage the client constructively, begin to work collaboratively toward agreed-on goals, build a trusting relationship, educate
the client about treatment, clarify and maintain the rules of the program,
and provide reassurance and practical help. For clients in precontemplation or contemplation, the primary objective is to build motivation.

Readings and Resources

Center for Substance Abuse Treatment. (2005). *Substance abuse treatment for
adults in the criminal justice system* (Technical Assistance Publication Series 44, DHHS Publication No. SMA 05-4056). Rockville, MD: Substance
Abuse and Mental Health Services Administration.

This Technical Assistance Publication provides a good overview of the relationship between the criminal justice system and substance abuse treatment and
offers many practical suggestions for counselors working with clients involved
in the criminal justice system.

Exercises

You can choose from a number of role-plays on the topic of monitoring
drug use:

E.6.1. Monitoring Drug Use Role-Plays

a. Rehearse asking the client, "So when did you use drugs last?" One
member of the team role-plays the client, and another member role-
plays the counselor.
b. Practice presenting the rationale for urinalysis to a member of your
team role-playing a client. (If you work at a clinic, be sure to state,
along with the rationale, the clinic's policy about consequences for
positive urinalysis results.)
c. Role-play a client's first positive urine test. One member of the team
role-plays the client, and another member role-plays the counselor.

d. Role-play a client's sixth positive urine test. One member of the team role-plays the client, and another member role-plays the counselor. All steps of this exercise will be a part of the workbook log. Be sure that the observers keep a detailed record of the dialogue.

E.6.2. Goal Setting When Client and Counselor Disagree on Goals

A client is actively using drugs but feels that his current job is causing the pressure that makes him use. He intends to seek a job with less pressure. You feel that he is not able to make a good decision while still actively using drugs. What would be your first goal with this client? What strategies and techniques would you use? This will be a part of the workbook log.

E.6.3. Strategies and Techniques for Coerced Clients

Imagine that a coerced client is resistant to discussing his drug use. What goal would you have with this client? What strategies and techniques would you use? This will be a part of the workbook log.

E.6.4. Decisional Balance Role-Play

Enact a decisional balance role-play. One person role-plays a client in the ambivalent phase, and another person role-plays the counselor, who tries to create a decisional balance for the client. This will be a part of the workbook log. Be sure that the observers keep a detailed record of the dialogue.

Chapter 7

The Middle Phase of Treatment

This chapter focuses on the middle phase of treatment. If the client has made good progress, the counselor can introduce new goals and use different techniques from the opening phase of treatment. The following goals and techniques are discussed in this chapter: relapse prevention; coping skills training; 12-step facilitation and the use of other self-help; examination of lifestyle, goals, and career; exploration of factors associated with the client's substance abuse; and discussion of termination.

The middle phase of treatment can be viewed in two ways: First, it marks the halfway point of the therapy, regardless of progress achieved. Second, it is the stage that comes after the successful completion of the earlier stages (the first five stages of treatment are discussed in Chapter 2). From this latter perspective, one can expect the following:

- The client by now is well motivated.
- The client is in the action or maintenance stage.
- The client is abstinent or has reduced his or her substance use to consistently safe levels.
- The counselor and client have a good working relationship.

If the above conditions are met, the role of the counselor shifts at this point. He or she becomes a coach, helping the client problem solve, anticipating problems, and providing encouragement. The counselor can monitor the client's progress and support him or her but otherwise let the client take the reins. In this phase of treatment, clients begin to test their own judgment and broaden their horizons: They may examine their life, career, and lifestyle and develop outside interests and friends. Clients at this point are much more able to stand on their own two feet and are less dependent on the counselor. This independence is healthy, and it marks a shift in the relationship between counselor and client. The counselor must encourage this step and facilitate it. Of course, it is important to be alert for roadblocks, potential relapses, and other problems, but the counselor should keep these setbacks in perspective. If the client is on the right track, relax. This stage of treatment is much like teaching a child to ride a bicycle; eventually, you no longer have to run alongside to make sure he or she doesn't fall.

If by the halfway point the client has not progressed in the areas listed above, however, the counselor must focus on these issues before moving on. For example, if the client is still in the precontemplation or contemplation stage, the counselor must help him or her move up to the action stage. If the client has not established abstinence or reduced his or her substance use to safe levels, the counselor must focus on helping him or her achieve this goal before working on the middle-phase aspects of counseling. If the counselor and client do not have a good working relationship, the counselor must use all of his or her skill to overcome this roadblock. This is a challenging task and a topic for advanced counseling texts, but I offer two suggestions to give you an idea of how to work on this. You may point out that the client does not seem to find you helpful (or whatever you notice) and ask whether there is something you can do to overcome this problem. Alternatively, you may develop a "work-around." For example, if you realize that your client really gets defensive when you become authoritative in tone, you can work to get your point across in a different manner. If all else fails, you can suggest that a different counselor might be more helpful. The remainder of the chapter details the approaches counselors can take with clients who have been successful in completing the earlier stages of treatment as outlined above.

Relapse Prevention

You will recall from Chapter 2 that relapse is the rule rather than the exception for substance abuse clients. Thus, attention to relapse is important. Relapse prevention is an aspect of substance abuse counseling that focuses on helping the client keep from using drugs and alcohol at all, if abstinence is the goal, or excessively, if harm reduction is the goal.

From this perspective, let's review the client's treatment experience up to this point. The effort to stop using the substance can seem monumental to the client. He or she probably had to make a number of wrenching decisions and take difficult actions. Once the client has achieved abstinence, he or she may feel enormous relief and a sense of accomplishment, which sometimes leads to a feeling of false confidence. AA calls this the "pink cloud." At this time, clients often want to leave treatment, although the counselor feels they are not ready. The client probably has not yet developed relapse prevention and other skills to stay abstinent or in remission.

Relapse potential is high when the client is in this state of mind. In this vein, Prochaska (1999) stated,

> A common reason that people relapse early in [the] action [phase] is that they are not well-prepared for the prolonged effort needed to progress to mainte- nance. Many think the worst is over in a few weeks or a few months. If they ease up on their efforts too early, they are at great risk for relapse. (p. 231)

Hence, relapse prevention logically fits into the treatment regimen at this point. Marlatt (1985) developed the concept of relapse prevention and the first treatment approach for it. The goal of relapse prevention is to anticipate and cope with the problem of relapse (Marlatt, 1985, p. 3). The relapse process is considered the end stage of decisions and actions that the client may not be fully aware of. The rationale for relapse prevention training is that clients can be made aware of these hidden processes and learn skills to counter them.

Relapse prevention training can be provided individually or in groups. In the training, clients identify high-risk situations for relapse (Marlatt, 1985, p. 54). They are taught to anticipate high-risk situations and avoid them if possible, and they learn skills to cope when such situations occur (Kadden & Cooney, 2005). Additionally, relaxation training and stress management training are of- fered (Marlatt, 1985, p. 56). The client's current lifestyle is reviewed for balance and stress. For clients whose lifestyle is out of balance or otherwise presents a risk for relapse, suggestions are made so they can reach a more balanced, absti- nence-promoting lifestyle (Marlatt, 1985, p. 60) through, for example, physical exercise and relaxation training (Haug, Sorensen, Gruber, & Song, 2005). Train- ing is also provided to limit the extent and damage of any lapse or relapse.

Coping Skills Training

Coping skills training is a kind of CBT (Monti, Kadden, Rohsenow, Cooney, & Abrams, 2002). The rationale for this approach is that people with sub- stance use disorders often do not have good coping mechanisms to deal with various tasks of daily living. This lack of coping skills likely played a part in their substance use and makes them vulnerable to relapse once they become sober. Therefore, training in coping skills makes sense in the middle phase of treatment. This training can be provided in groups and consists of specific, commonsense guidance on how to negotiate specific challenges, followed by clients' rehearsal of the skill. Topics include asser- tiveness training, drink refusal skills, resolution of relationship problems, anger management, and management of negative thinking.

12-Step Facilitation Approach to the Middle Phase of Treatment and the Use of Other Self-Help

Some clients who have successfully entered the middle phase of treat- ment are quite active in AA or NA. Their participation often entails more than just attending meetings. They may "qualify" at AA or NA meetings, where they tell the story of their alcoholism and recovery; they may help a particular new AA or NA member learn about sobriety (i.e., sponsorship); or they may volunteer to set up the chairs or make coffee for the meetings. Such activities are known as "giving service" in AA and NA. Clients may strive to use the steps of AA and NA to make their life more meaningful and anchor their sobriety; this is known as "working the steps." Clients who do this are creating a place to continue their work or sobriety after they leave treatment.

Counselors in recovery can offer their own wisdom garnered from AA or NA to their clients who are active in the program. They should make clear, however, that they cannot be sponsors for their clients, because they must protect the professional relationship from any potential complications. Counselors who are not familiar with AA, NA, and other self-help groups should learn about them. Several readings can help, but this research should be supplemented by attendance at open AA and NA meetings, where you will gain an appreciation of the powerful healing atmosphere of the "rooms" (AA and NA meetings). AA and NA meetings are free, and many are open to the public. If you observe a meeting, it is essential that, as a future counselor, you maintain respect for those attending and abide by the principle of anonymity: That is, respect the privacy of all those in attendance. Research has shown that AA and NA are successful approaches to recovery (Yalisove, 2004). Thus, counselors should discuss the programs with every client. Other self-help groups for helping people overcome their addictions are listed at the end of the chapter, along with their Web addresses.

Examining Lifestyle, Goals, and Career

Another important aspect of the middle phase of treatment is that clients and counselors have a chance to "breathe" and look at the big picture of the client's life. Clients in this phase likely do not have constant crises to confront, are stably abstinent, and thus have the resources to gain some perspective on their life and where they want to go. They have the opportunity to look at their lifestyle and at any issues that threaten their current adjustment. They can examine their marital or romantic relationships and their career. Clients may be in a dead-end job; they may want additional education or a new career. Counselors should encourage their clients to better themselves while helping them keep a realistic perspective. They may benefit from a referral to a career counselor. If such a referral is not possible, counselors can encourage their clients to find out the educational requirements for a new career they are considering and help them explore whether they have the motivation and stamina to follow through and the skills, aptitudes, and other needed resources to complete the education. Once clients make a commitment to the career move, counselors should provide encouragement.

If the client's current lifestyle poses risks for recovery (e.g., the client is dealing drugs, engaging in prostitution, or living with a person with an active substance use disorder), the counselor must skillfully address this problem. In such a situation, counselors and clients may disagree on the appropriate goal. The MI approach in this case is to anticipate difficulties, brainstorm about possible solutions, and let the client decide what to do. For example, clients with alcohol dependence sometimes continue to bartend or work in a liquor store. This might seem to be a set-up for relapse, yet I have seen several clients do well in recovery in such environments. Clients may actually use this situation to reinforce sobriety: They can see in vivid detail what alcohol is doing to their patrons.

In the following imagined dialogue, a counselor finds a way to help a client think about the dangers she might face in her current lifestyle:

Client: I'm so proud of being sober for 90 days.
Counselor: Congratulations—that's quite an achievement.
Client: I've decided to see a few of my old johns [men who pay for sex]. Only the ones who treat me well. I really need the money.
Counselor: This is your old line of work.
Client: Yeah.
Counselor: Let's look at the pros and cons of doing this.
Client: Okay.

The counselor might be tempted to jump in and say how much a return to prostitution would threaten the client's hard-won, newly established sobriety. But doing so probably would engage her resistance. By looking at the pros and cons, the client can begin to see what her plan entails and anticipate how it could threaten her sobriety.

Values Clarification

Some clients have lived by "street" values or "getting over" during the time they were actively using drugs and alcohol ("getting over" involves deceiving others to gain an advantage, usually money; e.g., a person might devise a compelling story about his or her need for a specific sum of money but, in fact, use the money to obtain drugs or alcohol). They might never really have thought about a different way of living. It is appropriate in the middle phase of treatment to introduce the client to other ways of living and working and to point out the advantages, but it is not fruitful to moralize or judge the client.

Some clients place a value on "beating the system." For example, they may work only long enough to obtain unemployment benefits, and only when the benefits expire do they consider work again. The value to these clients is that they maximize "free money." In my practice, I do not argue with the client that this is wrong. Instead, I point out the disadvantages of this approach to obtaining income in comparison with steady employment. It is the client's choice to change his or her way of earning money.

Examining Factors Associated With Substance Use Disorders

In some cases, specific personal factors pushed clients toward a substance use disorder or maintained that disorder—for example, anger, depression, childhood sexual abuse or other trauma, rivalry with an older sibling, the death of a parent when the client was a child, sexual problems, or a sense of inferiority. Counselors should use the middle phase of treatment to review with their clients the possibility of such factors. If such issues exist, they can be explored and discussed. Sometimes airing the problem to a sympathetic listener is enough to resolve it sufficiently so that it does not interfere with abstinence. If the problem continues to bother the client, encourage him or her to consider a referral to another mental health professional with the appropriate expertise. Substance abuse counselors should not try to treat deep-rooted psychological problems.

Letting Go: Part 1

At the halfway point of treatment, it is not too early to think about termination. Mentioning the time remaining to work makes sense. At this point, it is especially important to promote self-efficacy and respect clients' autonomy. Provided that the counselor believes in the clients' progress, he or she needs to help them believe in themselves and their ability to remain abstinent, problem solve, cope, and thrive on their own after the counseling has stopped (Tallman & Bohart, 1999). As clients have successes, counselors can reinforce them. The counselor can encourage the client's efforts to solve problems, think about the future, and make decisions. He or she can trust the client's judgments when they seem sound.

Counselors may have difficulty releasing control of their clients at this point; they may not be responsive to client growth, or they may be overly cautious about letting clients make their own choices and even mistakes. Alternatively, counselors may do the opposite. When clients begin to stand on their own, some counselors may lose interest in them and fail to provide guidance and support. It is important to be alert for these very human tendencies and work to overcome them.

In the middle phase of treatment, the counselor still has an important role to play for the client. One of the most critical things the counselor can do at this point is to help clients anticipate the outcomes of important matters. For example, clients may need help seeing the potential consequences of the various decisions they are considering as well as potential problems that they might have ignored up to this point. The therapeutic dyad now has a shared history of experience that the counselor can draw on in bringing such matters to the client's attention. Nevertheless, the counselor needs to respect the client's autonomy, especially given that the client will be on his or her own in a relatively short time. For example, consider the following scenario:

Evelyn has had 3 months of abstinence and is doing well in recovery, but she has not yet addressed any of the concerns she has about her boyfriend, who is actively using drugs. The counselor has decided that now is a good time to raise the issue of the boyfriend:

> *Counselor:* Evelyn, you've done a great job getting sober and beginning to think about school. You know, I've been wondering how your boyfriend fits into your new lifestyle. What are your thoughts about that?
> *Client:* He's the father of my daughter.
> *Counselor:* And he really loves Clara, doesn't he?
> *Client:* Yes. . . . But sometimes when he gets high, he acts stupid around her.

The counselor brings up his concern about the substance-using boyfriend with an open question, hoping that the client will mention her concerns. In this example, she does. Now the counselor need say very little:

> *Counselor:* What does he do?
> *Client:* He wakes her up and throws her up in the air. She gets way too excited. She can't sleep for the rest of the night.

After eliciting other concerns, the counselor can reflect, "It sounds like you are concerned about your boyfriend's ability to be a good parent to Clara." The counselor can then continue the process by problem solving with the client. This approach has the advantage of empowering the client, which becomes more and more important as the counseling moves toward termination.

Readings and Resources

Alcoholics Anonymous World Services. (1981). *Twelve steps and twelve traditions.* New York: Author.

This small book explains what the 12 steps of AA mean and how members can use them. It also describes the 12 traditions, the principles by which the organization runs.

Hubble, M. A., Duncan, B. L., & Miller, S. D. (Eds.). (1999). *The heart and soul of change: What works in therapy.* Washington, DC: American Psychological Association.

This book gives an accessible introduction to the discussion of the counselor–client relationship.

Marlatt, G. A., & Gordon, J. R. (Eds.). (1985). *Relapse prevention.* New York: Guilford Press.

This major and pioneering book on relapse prevention includes the theory and rationale for relapse prevention and outlines the treatment approach.

Monti, P. M., Kadden, R. M., Rohsenow, D. J., Cooney, N. L., & Abrams, D. B. (2002). *Treating alcohol dependence: A coping skills training guide.* New York: Guilford Press.

This is a practical guide to conducting coping skills training in substance abuse treatment settings.

Narcotics Anonymous World Service Office. (1988). *Narcotics Anonymous.* Van Nuys, CA: Author.

This is the main text for NA.

Norcross, J. C. (Ed.). (2002). *Psychotherapy relationships that work.* New York: Oxford University Press.

This book provides a good overview of the healing aspects of the relationship between the therapist and the patient. It includes a summary of research support for the importance of the therapeutic relationship and contains chapters on several important factors in nurturing that relationship.

Self-Help Web Sites

AA is the largest, oldest, and best known self-help group; its meetings are conducted all over the world. Al-Anon and Alateen, which are related to AA by affiliation, use the same 12 steps and 12 traditions for significant others of alcoholics. NA is a version of AA for people who abuse substances other than alcohol; it uses the 12 steps and traditions of AA. The other self-help organizations are much smaller.

- AA: www.alcoholics-anonymous.org/?Media=PlayFlash
- Al-Anon and Alateen: www.al-anon.alateen.org/
- NA: www.na.org/
- Moderation Management: www.moderation.org/
- Rational Recovery: www.rational.org/
- Smart Recovery: www.smartrecovery.org/

Exercises

E.7.1. Attend a Self-Help Meeting

Attend an open AA or NA meeting. Observe what happens. Write your reflections as soon as possible after the meeting; in your notes, respect the privacy of all attendees by making sure that no one can be identified. What was the format of the meeting? What factors did you see that promoted recovery? What negative factors did you see? What difficulties might your clients have with (a) attending their first meeting and then (b) staying active in AA or NA? This will be a part of the workbook log.

E.7.2. Relapse Prevention Role-Play

In this relapse prevention role-play, the counselor asks the client to talk about factors that would put him or her at risk for a relapse and begins a discussion of how to overcome one of the risks. One member of the team role-plays the client, and another member role-plays the counselor. This will be a part of the workbook log. Be sure that the observers keep a detailed record of the dialogue.

E.7.3. Role-Play: Client Wants to Leave Treatment Prematurely

Role-play the following scenario: The client has successfully remained abstinent for 90 days and has decided that he or she no longer needs treatment. This role-play should have two parts: In the first part, try to convince the client to remain in treatment; in the second part of the role-play, the client insists on leaving. Develop goals for both scenarios. One member of the team role-plays the client, and another member role-plays the counselor. This will be a part of the workbook log. Be sure that the observers keep a detailed record of the dialogue. The team should discuss the goals and techniques to be used before beginning the role-play.

E.7.4. Dialogue and Role-Play: Client Challenges

Role-play the following scenario: The client has been abstinent for 3 months, after 6 months in treatment. He or she will be starting college in 3 weeks. One member of the team role-plays the client, and another member role-plays the counselor. This will be a part of the workbook log. Be sure that the observers keep a detailed record of the dialogue.

E.7.5. Role-Play: Client Decides to Resume Sex Work

Review the dialogue in this chapter regarding the client who is 90 days abstinent and announces her plan to resume sex work. Set up a role-play to continue the dialogue. One member of the team role-plays the client, and another member role-plays the counselor. This will be a part of the workbook log. Be sure that the observers keep a detailed record of the dialogue.

Chapter 8

Moving Toward Termination

The termination phase is a dynamic and important aspect of treatment and requires a number of counseling skills, which are discussed in this chapter. Topics included in this chapter are dealing with the emotional factors experienced by the client and counselor in termination, criteria for successful termination, circumstances of termination, the stages of change and termination, preparing the client for continuing on his or her own, and saying goodbye. Ideally, treatment ends when the client has made good progress and is ready to function without counseling. Most of the time, however, treatment ends because the client chooses to leave early or because of external factors, such as agency policies, insurance coverage, eligibility for treatment, or other administrative reasons. This complication is discussed.

Termination of counseling means the end of a relationship, a status, and a process. The client must give up the counselor, the status of patient, and the process of working with the counselor. The counselor hopes that clients will apply what they have learned in counseling on their own, as they must now remain abstinent, solve problems, make decisions, and weather crises without the counselor's help. Termination should be considered a process rather than an event. It corresponds to Phases 7 and 8 of the stages of therapy discussed in Chapter 2. Clients should be prepared for termination several sessions before the last session.

Letting Go: Part 2

In the termination phase, the counselor must constructively let go of the client. This process is more likely to go smoothly if the counselor has followed the principle of respecting the client's autonomy from the beginning of treatment. This approach lets clients see that they are responsible for any changes they make. If the counselor fails to clarify the client's responsibility for change, both client and counselor may feel the counselor is responsible for the changes. When this happens, it puts a strain on termination, because the client and possibly the counselor may be fearful that the client will not be able to continue making progress on his or her own. When clients leave before they are fully prepared, which is fairly common, counselors must keep in mind what they can realistically do, be as helpful as possible, and let go. Counselors in recovery may need to explain to some clients that they cannot become their clients' AA or NA sponsors even after termination.

To get some idea of what the end phase of counseling is like from your own life experience, consider what it was like to say goodbye to a good teacher. You might have felt both sad and grateful. If the teacher taught a successful class, though, you probably felt reasonably confident that you could apply the skills you learned from him or her in your next class.

Criteria for Successful Termination

How can a counselor know when it is time to stop counseling with clients? The primary objective in substance abuse counseling is to provide the tools for the client to stay sober on his or her own. Alternatively, in some instances, a harm reduction goal is appropriate. The following are some guidelines for termination:

1. In the last several months of treatment, the client has been—and remains—stably abstinent or consistently using substances at safe levels (i.e., maintenance stage of change).
2. The client is active in and committed to self-help involvement.
3. The client has social relationships that are supportive of recovery, such as a spouse or parent.
4. The client has developed and uses relapse prevention skills, coping skills, and problem-solving skills.
5. If the client has underlying psychological issues, he or she has dealt with those issues so they do not interfere with abstinence.
6. The client's lifestyle is consistent with sobriety.

Rarely, however, are all goals fully met in counseling (Ward, 1984), and counselors must develop a good perspective on this. Typically, clients wish to leave treatment before counselors feel the clients are ready. In this vein, Hunsley, Aubry, and Verstervelt (1999) reported that clients surveyed after treatment were more likely to state that they had completed their goals than their therapists were. Counselors must work collaboratively with their clients to determine when the counseling process should end. They need to balance their view of their clients' remaining therapeutic goals with respect for their clients' autonomy and the importance of ending counseling on a positive and collaborative note. If the termination is determined by external factors, such as insurance coverage, it is better to help clients prepare for termination than to rail against the system.

Circumstances of Termination

Termination occurs under two conditions: premature termination, and termination on completion of treatment goals. Because the tasks of the counselor are affected by these conditions, each kind is discussed separately.

Premature Termination

A large percentage of clients in substance abuse clinics leave before completing treatment (Jacobson, 2004). Thus, counselors must be prepared to discuss termination with clients in the most therapeutic manner possible under these circumstances. Obviously, the first objective is to encourage the client to complete treatment.

If you are unable to get the client to stay in treatment or if he or she cannot stay, your goal is to keep the door open, consolidate what gains have been made, and keep treatment a desirable option for the client. Counselors may be tempted to warn clients about the dangers of leaving treatment early or feel obligated to provide their expertise about the consequences of leaving early. From the perspective of MI, it is important that the counselor couch his or her remarks tactfully in this regard. It is far better to say, "I am concerned about you leaving at this time because you haven't had time to really develop these new tools you have been learning to help you stay sober. What do you think?" than, "If you leave treatment now, I can almost guarantee that you are going to relapse, given my professional experience."

If the client decides to leave treatment prematurely despite the counselor's best efforts, the counselor can summarize the progress the client has made and keep the door open. For example, to a client who has decided to leave treatment after three sessions, the counselor could say the following:

Counselor: I appreciate that you decided to come in and discuss this with me. If you think it would be helpful, I'd like to summarize our progress together.
Client: Okay.
Counselor: You've remained sober for 3 weeks, you've come to your sessions, you have some idea of what it's like to be sober.
Client: Yeah. Well, that's true. But, you know, I believe that a person needs to take actions and not just talk about things. So I want to do it on my own.
Counselor: I can understand that. Good luck with your efforts. If you have difficulties, a relapse, or other problems, the door is open for you to resume your sessions. I'd like to hear how you're doing. Would you give me a call in 2 weeks?

Client: Okay.
Counselor: I'll mark it in my calendar, March 25.

In some cases, termination may be forced because a client has violated agency policy—for instance, by becoming intoxicated in an inpatient rehabilitation facility. When this happens, the counselor's goal is much the same as above. The discharge is not a punishment but a required sanction. Referral and guidance should be provided if the client is receptive.

Premature terminations are often difficult for counselors to handle, for a number of reasons: The rug is being pulled out from under the counselor's efforts, and he or she may be caught off guard. The counselor may feel genuine concern for the client's welfare, think that the client is making a mistake, or believe an exception should be made to the clinic's rules if the client is being discharged for administrative reasons. The counselor may even feel that he or she failed the client. It is important to acknowledge such reactions to oneself but then summon the ability to focus on what is best for the client.

Termination on Completion

Discussing termination with a client who has successfully completed treatment can be an enjoyable experience for both the client and the counselor. For these clients, you should summarize gains, tools learned, and other progress the client has made. Discuss potential obstacles and how they could be dealt with. Also, ask how the client feels about leaving and any concerns he or she has. Allow the full airing of these feelings and concerns, and problem solve them if necessary. If more time is needed, postpone termination. Help the client envision life after treatment, and keep the door open; a relapse plan should be in place. These suggestions are discussed in more detail in The Last Few Sessions: Passing the Baton to the Client, later in the chapter.

In many cases, the length of stay in treatment is predetermined. Some programs have a standard length of stay, such as a 28-day inpatient program or a 6-month therapeutic community. Managed care may also dictate the length of stay. In these situations, the counselor must anticipate the termination and prepare for it much as described above.

The Stages of Change and Termination

When clients leave treatment, they should, ideally, be in the maintenance phase of change and so stably abstinent. If the client is not in this phase, the termination goals must be modified accordingly. Research has shown that precontemplators are most likely to terminate prematurely (Brogan, Prochaska, & Prochaska, 1999), but clients may choose or be obligated to leave treatment while in any of the other stages of change. In these instances, any positive steps the client has taken should be noted. The termination process for clients who are not in maintenance should take into consideration their current stage of change and focus on the next step in their recovery. It is not useful to list all of the steps the client must take to get sober; this could be overwhelming and discouraging. For example, the following is an imaginary dialogue between a counselor and a client in contemplation who is leaving treatment:

> *Counselor:* You know, Bill, we've worked for several months together. In that time, we have looked at your use of marijuana. We've seen the good aspects of marijuana and the bad aspects. At this time, you haven't decided whether you need to stop or cut down your use. Because you have to stop coming here in a few weeks, I would like to offer some suggestions.
>
> *Client:* Sure.
>
> *Counselor:* I guess the main thing I would suggest is that you continue the process we've begun so that you can make a decision you're happy with about using marijuana. This means continuing to look at the pros and cons of use. If you would like help with that, give me a call, and I'd be happy to see you again, or, if you prefer, I can find a good referral for you. Do you have any questions?
>
> *Client:* My wife thinks I should stop, but I'm still up in the air.
>
> *Counselor:* That's just the point; we have to stop before you're going to resolve this dilemma. You can see some negatives, like it hurts your relationship with your wife, but you still find some enjoyable aspects of using marijuana. The thing for you to focus on is finding a way to make a decision about this that you will be happy with.
>
> *Client:* That makes sense.
>
> *Counselor:* Would you like to call me in a month to let me know how you're doing?
>
> *Client:* Okay.
>
> *Counselor:* How about March 25? I'll mark it in my calendar.

Similarly, when clients are in the determination or action stage when they leave treatment, the counselor should help them focus on the next step they need to take to overcome their addictions.

The Last Few Sessions: Passing the Baton to the Client

The last three or four sessions are used to address how the client will manage on his or her own after the treatment ends. The following steps will help the client with this task.

Review and Summarize Progress

Discuss what the client was like when he or she first started and how he or she has changed. Highlight the positive steps the client has made, and give him or her positive feedback about those steps.

Assess the Client's Current Status

State how long the client has been abstinent, and discuss his or her current adjustment to work, family, and other areas of his or her life. Emphasize the strengths of the client's current adjustment, but be sure to note areas of concern.

Summarize the Skills the Client Has Learned

Discuss the coping skills the client has developed, including relapse prevention skills, problem-solving skills, supportive sober relationships he or she has developed, self-help groups he or she has joined, and any other skills that help him or her stay abstinent.

Develop a Plan With the Client That Helps Him or Her Maintain Abstinence Once Counseling Stops

This is essentially a treatment plan for after treatment; it is often called an aftercare plan. Discuss with the client what he or she can do to maintain abstinence. The planned approach may include getting involved with self-help organizations, seeking out and maintaining social relationships that are supportive of recovery, and making further lifestyle adjustments. Review the skills the client has learned to support his or her recovery, and discuss which ones he or she will make use of. For example, to develop this plan you can ask clients, "What will help you keep the ball rolling in the positive direction you're going in once you leave treatment?"

Anticipate Potential Problems

Clients—even those who terminate in the maintenance phase—often leave treatment with lingering ambivalence about their drug use. This must be acknowledged as an ongoing issue that the client must confront (Sellman et al., 2007). Discuss what the client will do when he or she has urges to use drugs or alcohol. Both you and the client will probably be aware of life events that may pose risks for a relapse. Review them with the client, and discuss some of the options that he or she could use to deal with them. Remind the client that relapse is an aspect of the disorder and that, should he or she lapse or relapse, he or she is welcome to return to treatment. For example, to anticipate potential problems, you could ask clients, "What could go wrong with our plan?" Follow this question up with, "How can we protect against that?"

Discuss the Client's Fears and Concerns About Termination, and Help Resolve Them

Ask the client directly about his or her fears and concerns about leaving, and then address them. If the client is concerned about whether he or she can remain abstinent, review these concerns, discuss what tools the client has, and if you feel confident that the client is well prepared, say so. Reassure the client that it is natural to have concerns about maintaining abstinence. If you are not confident about the client's ability to remain abstinent, take the time to review his or her aftercare plan carefully, offer additional sessions if possible, and develop a relapse plan. A relapse plan details what positive steps the client will take if he or she begins to misuse substances. It may be as simple as calling a sponsor or supportive family member or resuming treatment in the case of a relapse.

Encourage Follow-Up Sessions

No matter how certain you and the client are that the client will remain abstinent, encourage some form of follow-up. Recommend at least one session a month for 6 months. If the client does not want to do that, encourage him or her to call you on a specific date. Assure the client that you would welcome him or her back for additional sessions.

Saying Goodbye

Clients react to termination in a number of ways. Many are grateful for the help they have received; others may not feel confident that they can be successful on their own and may become fearful and insist that they need more treatment. Some may relapse or fall back on other negative patterns. Others may devalue the treatment they have received (Bostic, Shadid, & Blotcky, 1996). Counselors may react to termination in a number of ways as well: For example, they may avoid bringing up the topic, or they may not realize how important they and the counseling have been for the client (Bostic et al., 1996). My point is that termination represents the end of a relationship. In this case the relationship is a professional one, but, nonetheless, there may be an emotional attachment between the counselor and client. This is to be expected, but counselors need to be alert to their clients' and their own reactions, which may catch them off guard. These emotional reactions, if not discussed, can lead to premature termination, acting out before termination, depreciation of therapy, and lapse or relapse into substance use.

Goodbyes are important; they can be emotional and meaningful. When the work has been productive and rewarding to both participants, counselors can talk about it. Clients should be congratulated on work well done. If the work has not gone well, one can be honest without being overly critical. Research indicates that counselors have difficulty acknowledging when counseling has not gone as they hoped (Hunsley et al., 1999). The counseling process is not a purely technical procedure, and compatibility between counselor and client cannot always be ensured. Thus, a discussion of what the client would like in his or her next counselor or treatment episode could be useful as part of the termination discussion when the relationship between the client and counselor has not gone well, as illustrated in the following imagined dialogue:

Counselor: Joe, we will have to finish our sessions in the next 2 weeks. I would like to summarize our work. You have made some progress by reducing your use of drugs at times. Still, you are not convinced that you have a drug problem. I think the next thing for you to do is to figure out whether you really do have a drug problem. Coming back to counseling could help you with that. I'd like to ask you what you thought was helpful here and, if you resume counseling, what you would look for in your next counselor.

Whatever the manner and kind of termination, how you handle it can either enhance the gains of the client or undermine them. If you show appropriate confidence in the client and provide him or her with encouragement, that will build his or her confidence. Conversely, if progress has been limited, you must be realistic without being overly negative. At the very least, it is important not to do anything that would discourage the patient from resuming treatment in the future.

Exercises

E.8.1. Goodbyes

Think about situations in which you had to say goodbye. What was the best? What was the worst? What were the reasons? How might these experiences relate to termination in counseling? This will be a part of the workbook log.

E.8.2. Treatment Termination Goal Setting

Some clients are in contemplation, determination, or action when treatment must be terminated. What goals should the counselor focus on for clients in these stages of change? Role-play a client in the last session in contemplation, determination, or action; one person role-plays the counselor. This will be a part of the workbook log. Be sure that the observers keep a detailed record of the dialogue. The team should discuss the goals and techniques to be used before beginning the role-play.

E.8.3. Role-Play Treatment Termination Scenarios

Role-play a scenario in which a client has decided to leave treatment after three sessions and get sober on his or her own. One team member role-plays the client, and one team member role-plays the counselor. This role-play should have two parts: In the first part, try to convince the client to remain in treatment; in the second part of the role-play, the client insists on leaving. Develop goals for that possibility, and then role-play it. This will be a part of the workbook log. Be sure that the observers keep a detailed record of the dialogue. The team should discuss the goals and techniques to be used before beginning the role-play.

E.8.4. Discharge Role-Play

Role-play a scenario in which a client has been found high on drugs in a residential rehabilitation facility. He or she has slept for several hours and now will see his or her primary counselor, who must discuss the client's discharge from the facility. One team member role-plays the client, and one team member role-plays the counselor. This will be a part of the workbook log. Be sure that the observers keep a detailed record of the dialogue. The team should discuss the goals and techniques to be used before beginning the role-play.

Chapter 9

Group Counseling for Clients With Substance Use Disorders

Richard Kempter

Given that most substance abuse programs offer group counseling, substance abuse counselors need to develop good group counseling skills. This chapter focuses on the interactional or interpersonal method of group counseling for clients with substance use disorders. In interactional groups, the primary mode of change is through group interaction, not interaction between the members and the facilitator. This chapter provides a basic framework for understanding interactional group counseling, describes its main functions, and explains why it is so helpful to clients.

Interactional group counseling is very powerful, because the healing process results from member interactions. The facilitator has to get out of the way of the group members' interaction and set the stage for peer-to-peer healing. Clients with substance use disorders often isolate or dominate in relationships, but by interacting with other members in the group, they learn to negotiate and compromise, and they develop healthy relationships. As a result, they spend less time trying to manipulate and are more open to their peers' input. The more positive group interaction that occurs, the greater the positive influence members have on each other.

The model presented in this chapter is different from individual counseling in a group setting or a teaching model, wherein the facilitator primarily interacts with the group members. In the latter models, the flow of group action is between the members and the facilitator, not among the members. Interactional counseling groups require a set of group facilitator skills different from the more commonly taught teacher–student interaction methods. One must not assume that knowledge of teaching methods equals knowledge of interactional methods. Thus, classroom instruction, topic discussion, and instruction manual exercises (e.g., relapse prevention triggers) are not the focus of this chapter.

Basic Elements of Group Counseling

The basic elements of group counseling include creating group cohesion, setting boundaries, developing commitment for the group, providing confidentiality, keeping the group in the "here and now," ensuring safety and self-disclosure, and expressing emotion. Each element is discussed in the sections that follow.

Group Cohesion

Group cohesion is a sense of closeness, nurturing, and bonding among group members. It is fundamental to the healing process and only develops when members support, care for, and, most important, engage each other. When group cohesion exists, members can challenge each other on their negative behavior. How can the group leader facilitate group cohesion? He or she must allow members to interact and not rescue them from this process by lecturing or becoming the center of attention, although the group's discomfort level and anxiety may be high. The leader must foster the expression of feelings among group members, without taking away their uncomfortable emotions. Cultivating here-and-now, first-person (i.e., *I* and *you*) interactions, discussed below, encourages group cohesion.

Boundary Setting

For group process to be successful, the facilitator must provide a structure that promotes cohesion, commitment, and group solidarity. The most important guidelines are listed below.

Groups need to sit in a close circle, in a private room, squarely facing each other. Members frequently try to hide from the group by sitting outside the circle or wearing sunglasses or a visor to hide their face. This must not be allowed. In addition, because of resistance, discussed later in this chapter, members tend to avoid coming to group sessions. With rare exceptions, attendance must be mandatory and lateness not tolerated by the group. Once the group or the facilitator entertains excuses, the group is on a slippery slope, and the facilitator has no way to determine a legitimate excuse from an illegitimate one. The question of members' lateness or absence becomes a side show distracting attention from the real issue: what the member is avoiding by missing group. Clients with substance use disorders often have difficulty confronting their own shortcomings and frequently externalize their problems. If the group adheres to a strict attendance policy, members are forced to address their own issues. Finally, do not allow group members to leave during group (e.g., to go to the bathroom or get water) unless the group is having a long, marathon session.

Group leaders can choose from two ways to handle group member contact outside group sessions. One is to forbid any contact whatsoever, but that is often not realistic. A better approach is to allow contact but require that members bring back to the group any issues that originate because of outside contact and discuss them openly. Members often violate these rules, but they get caught at a later date, which leads to meaningful work.

Commitment

Commitment is vital to the work of the group. Clients avoid commitment for many reasons, but all spring from a desire to protect themselves from growth and change, which hinders the group's status as a safe place to learn and grow. Often, clients strive to protect themselves by having an "out" or an "escape hatch" to use when the going gets tough—for example, missing group or coming late. To overcome this attitude, leaders must demand that group members make a commitment. For example, a member may state, "I was sick." If the group does not reject that excuse, then the facilitator must confront the members for not caring about each other and for not caring whether a member misses group. He or she should tell the group members that if they do not care about each other—and accepting an excuse counts as not caring—then they do not have commitment.

Confidentiality

Although confidentiality is vital, the facilitator cannot guarantee that other group members will not reveal information to others. The facilitator can only promise that he or she will honor confidentiality. Group leaders should not claim that the group will be confidential, because they cannot speak for group members or control what those members say and to whom. The facilitator may raise the confidentiality issue, but the members should talk to each other about how they will handle these issues. Remember that the facilitator does not "lead a discussion" on confidentiality, because that would make the facilitator the center of attention, and that must not happen in an interactional group. For example, group members can share how they feel about revealing group members' names to outsiders.

Confidentiality needs to be discussed early on in the group; otherwise, members may falsely assume that some form of confidentiality exists and then blame the facilitator if a breach occurs. Clients must be told that confidentiality is not absolute. For example, at a substance abuse agency, all members of the clinical team have access to all relevant client information.

Here and Now

Perhaps nothing more distinguishes interactional group counseling from other group counseling modalities than the concept of here and now versus there and then. *Here and now* refers to the present feelings group members have about each other and their interactions with each other. *There and then* means talking about the past and events that took place outside of the group, including storytelling, philosophizing, and relating general examples without being specific.

Here and now is very powerful, because it unfolds as it happens in a group. Group members display their personalities in the presence of the group, all their strengths and weaknesses. Others respond not to the member's storytelling but to how he or she behaves in group. Thus, group members cannot "run away," avoid, or fabricate stories, because all members are observing their present behavior. If a participant tries to isolate or dominate others, he or she is challenged by other group members. It is hard to fool group members, because they are responding to one's present behavior, not to some story of the past.

Safety and Self-Disclosure

Trust, risk taking, and self-disclosure go hand in hand. At the start of a new group, members immediately try to determine how to play it safe. In most social situations, this is common. For a group to be effective, however, the members must find a way to surrender their need to play it safe and must take some risks. Much of group behavior is plotted around members' efforts to protect themselves, but members are unaware of this process and do not address it directly. Clients with substance use disorders often have great difficulty with trust, assuming that all others are totally untrustworthy and the only way to survive is to manipulate people for their own benefit or to isolate themselves. Interactional groups provide participants an opportunity to revisit trust issues in a more open, constructive manner. As members are struggling with trust issues, bringing them out in the open gives the entire group a chance to share and participate in this important process. The leader should advise group members, "No need to jump into the water to take a big risk—put a toe in and see how the temperature is. Take small risks, but take risks—it is the process of risk taking that brings out so many group issues."

Clients with a substance use disorder commonly feel their secrets are nobody's business. Translated, this means that the group is not safe. When the group members can talk openly and directly about issues of safety, there is group movement. Feeling safe and supported in a group is almost always the foremost issue for all members. Talking about safety directly builds group support and cohesion.

Expression of Emotion

Emotions and feelings are at the heart of the group counseling process. Above all else, group process is an emotional education, which many clients with substance use disorders have never had. Most people have had years of rational education but lack emotional education. Both members and leaders gain emotional intelligence when they become aware of and learn how to control their feelings. *Emotional intelligence* means learning to express one's feelings by making a decision to do so rather than impulsively responding. Expressing emotions is a scary process in itself; it involves taking risks and putting oneself "out there." Emotional expression facilitates group bonding, increases member commitment, deepens group intimacy and trust, triggers emotions in others, helps members realize that their issues are shared and universal, reduces isolation, and provides insight.

Common Misconceptions About Interactional Groups

In general, people seem to have several misconceptions about interactional groups. One common misconception is that interpersonal groups are anti-intellectual (Corey, 1981). Although it is true that groups teach emotional intelligence, cognitive knowledge of group process is absolutely essential to a thorough understanding of group process and interpersonal behavior. Another misconception is that group sessions are a place to get emotionally high, a touchy-feely place. Although emotional closeness is a by-product of emotional expression, an emotional high is not a goal of groups. Many people also mistakenly believe that groups are meant to provide intimacy. Again, intimacy may be a by-product of emotional connections with others; it is not a goal in itself. It is also a mistake to view groups as a "cure all." There is no such thing as a panacea, but counseling groups can be a powerful change agent in clients' lives.

Another misconception is that groups lead to selfishness. The opposite is true; groups help members become less self-centered and more sensitive to others' feelings. People also often see groups as unreal and artificial. Although interpersonal counseling groups are different from comfortable work and family groups, they are a different reality, one in which members are more direct and open with each other. It is also a misconception that groups "brainwash" their members. Although groups do exert a good deal of pressure on their members, counseling groups strive for a balance between autonomy and group pressure, trying to be responsive to group influence yet maintain individual autonomy. This effort is a balancing act, a constant work in progress.

Interactional Group Leadership

An effective interactional facilitator stays out of the way of group process so the members can do the work. For most facilitators this is a new skill and must be learned. For interactional groups to prosper, the leader must not be the center of attention. He or she must not be the hub of the wheel (i.e., the center of focus), surrounded by members who individually talk to the leader as spokes of the wheel. Lecturing, interpreting, and giving advice are only minor functions for an interactional facilitator. For example, group silences are okay; the facilitator is not obligated to break them. In fact, what happens after a silence is often very salient. Once the group has learned to work on its own, the facilitator can come in and out of the action without being the center of focus. The most important method of leadership development in many groups is to be a member first.

A valuable role for the facilitator is to be an observer making group process comments. The leader may take on several roles, however, including coaching, refereeing, coercing, manipulating, persuading, and role modeling. For instance, if group members are having difficulty directly challenging each other, the facilitator can challenge a group member to model how it is done. *Coaching* involves, for example, directing, instructing, and training a group member to challenge or support another group member. An example of *refereeing* is resolving a conflict between two group members. *Coercing* means compelling a person to behave in an involuntary way (whether through action or inaction) by use of threats or intimidation. For example, if a client has threatened another group member, the facilitator may coerce this person into retreating and calming down. *Manipulation* involves shrewd management, not for the benefit of the facilitator but for the benefit of the client. If some deception is necessary for the good of the client, then the facilitator may do it. The point is, do not assume that honesty is the highest ethical level. The ultimate goal is for the client to improve. The facilitator uses *persuasion* to influence the group or individual members, such as by explaining why it is unproductive to use *we* language instead of *I* language.

In *role modeling*, facilitators do not explain what they are doing but directly take an action, such as challenging or supporting (giving positive feedback) to a specific group member, thus serving as role models in the hope that group members will copy the behavior. Modeling, demonstrating to the group how to respond as a member, is an important facilitator role. For example, the facilitator may give direct support and praise to a participant, setting the stage for other group members to follow suit. Such an example propels the group forward. The facilitator may confront a member directly on his or her negative behavior, thereby giving permission for the group members to do the same with each other. By the same token, facilitators should be prepared to be confronted by the group members.

Although the facilitator should not be a blank screen or take charge and be the locus of the group, as your leadership style emerges, strive for an active role without being the center of focus. Above all, the facilitator must not be aloof; you must respond as a real person, often reacting directly to members' confrontations (i.e., you must respond as a person, not interpret why you are being challenged). If you fail to answer challenges directly, the clients may lose respect for you, which will reduce your effectiveness as a facilitator. Most important, you must develop a therapeutic bond with clients. Forming human relationships and building a treatment alliance with members is vital for their growth. The leader needs to be a good listener, needs to be warm and caring, but also must be forceful when necessary and, of course, resist being manipulated. The challenge is to be responsive and compassionate but also set limits, which can feel contradictory and is not easy to do. The leader must admit mistakes and be open; not only does this model such behavior for members, but it develops closer group relationships and alliances.

Because group meetings are so powerful, the facilitator experiences many emotions during a session; therefore, he or she must have high emotional intelligence and be able to stay with his or her feelings and regulate them, then express them in a productive fashion in the group. Having high emotional intelligence does not mean staying in the cognitive realm but rather involves expressing one's feelings in a productive fashion. The facilitator need not justify or defend his or her behavior. Instead, he or she can use a "hit and run" tactic, making a comment that delivers a powerful punch, then dropping out so the group can react to it. This protects the facilitator from having to win a confrontation. Provoking clients can be a useful method, but having to win the battle is destructive. Facilitators must be able to tolerate their own and others' painful experiences and despair, for they will witness plenty of painful group experiences, accompanied by unpleasant emotions. That is, to be comfortable with being very uncomfortable, the leader must bring strength and a steady hand to the group. He or she needs to know how to develop trust in the group, particularly by not avoiding negative feelings but supporting the group in moving through these feelings and coming out on the other side. This is particularly crucial for clients with substance use disorders, because trust is often a major issue. The group battle is for control, but winning this battle is often a long-term struggle, not a single episode. The facilitator should not settle for mediocrity but ought to support and push the group to work hard. A good leader encourages members to give feedback to each other and make group process comments for members to act on.

The facilitator must earn credibility through the process of the group; it is not bestowed on the leader because of his or her title. In addition, although the group is in a constant struggle between group influence and autonomy, the facilitator must assist members in respecting the rights of others. Although some clients absolutely insist on being respected, they may behave disrespectfully to the facilitator. These clients are compelled to win the battle for respect. The facilitator must not engage in such a battle, because he or she will lose. That is, the facilitator must respect group members even when those members do not respect the facilitator. This concept is critical not only for the progress of treatment but also to protect the facilitator from assault. A stalemate is the best outcome when a battle for respect ensues between a group and the facilitator; at this point, treatment stops. Punishing the member for being disrespectful is counterproductive. Instead, respect the client, regardless of his or her disrespect for you.

Above all, the facilitator must instill hope in substance abuse counseling groups, because the members' past self-destructive behavior might have led to loss of hope. The facilitator must never give up hope, no matter how difficult the struggle or how limited the prognosis, because the hope of the facilitator often eventually wins the battle for positive change.

The Routine Tasks of Group Leaders

Beginning a New Group

When an interactional group begins, members as well as facilitators are usually quite uncomfortable; members do not know what to do in a group without direction or a topic to explore. This floundering about, however—the struggle to find a path—brings group cohesion. For members to be close, to care about each other, to help each other, to form a bond, they must first engage each other, often in a clumsy, uncomfortable manner. There is no way around it, but the outcome can be a solid, working, caring group. Group members may go to great lengths to avoid talking to each other (to play it safe) and giving each other feedback, because it is far safer not to talk directly to other group members; thus, they talk to the "air." They need help discussing just how unsafe they feel in group and what they are going to do about it. It is often new for members to focus directly on safety.

Beginning the Group Session

At the beginning of a group session, just announce that it is time to start the group, letting the members take the lead in getting the session going. Remember that the facilitator does not lead or teach the group, so there is no topic to discuss. Topics prevent the members from addressing each other and the group process; they serve as a safety valve, allowing the members to avoid each other. Remember that silence is okay. If the group silence is prolonged, then assist members in addressing, talking with, and engaging other group members. Keep in mind that the facilitator's focus is on group interaction.

Introducing New Members

Do not introduce new members—that takes the pressure off important group issues, and it puts the facilitator at center stage. Rather, just let a new member quietly join the session. If the participants do not speak to or comment on the new member, point out that they are ignoring him or her and ask why they are doing this. Is it because they do not want the new member there?

Keeping Track of Group Processes

First things first: Without complete attendance, there is no group. The same goes for lateness; it is extremely disruptive to the business of the group. Remember that the here and now keeps members engaged with each other, even though doing so is very uncomfortable and risky. The facilitator focuses not only on individual dynamics but on group process.

Ending the Group Session

Remember to end the group session on time. It is common for clients to bring up important concerns or become very emotional just as it is time for the group to end. In general, the facilitator needs to end the group on schedule regardless of the crisis; otherwise, a precedent is set for extended group sessions. This becomes a slippery slope, and members are unclear when the group should end. Participants may be stalling the end of the session as a test, to see whether the leader cares. If this happens, initiate a discussion about the fact that members wait until the end of the group to bring up important issues, and remind them to save these issues for the next group session. Encourage them to discuss how it makes them feel that the group session ended on time, how they feel toward the leader, and whether they see the leader as uncaring for ending the session on time.

Client Reactions to the Group and Group Leader

Clients with substance use disorders often enter the group with feelings of resentment and hostility; they frequently express animosity and resist group process. Group members often have strong emotional reactions to the leader, both positive and negative, that are colored by their past. Such reactions are called *transference* (Flores, 1997). Transference causes a person to see others as they are not and is rooted in the idea that the past distorts the present. It is a tendency to repeat the past by misconceiving the present. Transference is largely an unconscious process; group members do not realize they are doing it.

As a result of transference, members often see the facilitator in extremes, all good or all bad—warm, caring, and supportive or cold, callous, and distant. Of course, in reality, the facilitator may be either, but the strength and drive of the client's feelings toward the facilitator tell the story. Sudden onset of intense anger toward the facilitator may be transference, although there might also be truth to the group member's complaint. Transference can also be directed from one group member to another; members may remind each other of their siblings, spouses, or lovers, which can result in transference. This, in turn, may be the force behind competition and jealousy expressed among group members.

Transference is complex. Participants' attitudes toward the counselor are not always transference; some are based in reality. Nevertheless, group members must learn how they project their images of their parents and siblings onto the leader and other members and how these misperceptions are determined by their own childhood experiences and infantile distortions. Conflicted or negative parental relations have a lasting and distorting effect on present relationships. Transference reactions in a group crystallize around an element of truth about the leader, but the perception is twisted and exaggerated.

Transference can interfere with sobriety, precipitating a relapse, but it is a rich source of useful information. Under the sway of transference, some clients may claim that the facilitator is so bad they need to leave the group, or they may blame the facilitator for their relapse. Such transference reactions can give the facilitator insight into the origins of a client's self-destructive behavior patterns. Some group members project a negative transference onto other members or even the whole group. They may be convinced that others are the problem and that they would be fine if only they were left alone. Group consensual agreements counter these individual distortions. The support of group members steadies the course of group therapy because cohesion, trust, and safety are crucial.

Ignoring transference leads to misunderstanding. If the facilitator can help clients resolve their transference, clients can better understand their competitive, exploitative, sexual, and authority issues and their intimacy conflicts. Facilitators must not, however, force the content of conflicts or insist on having their way. In fact, sometimes if the facilitator pulls back, members are more able to address their own transference issues. Certainly, the facilitator must not become defensive or provocative toward a client who is under the sway of a transference reaction; this only escalates the transference. Instead, a hit-and-run approach may be useful, as described above.

The Group Leader and His or Her Emotional Reactions to the Group

Conducting groups is an intensely emotional experience, and the group leader must monitor his or her emotions to determine the best intervention for developing group process. It is common for group leaders to experience countertransference—that is, feelings from their own history evoked by the emotion of the group (Levine, 1993). Countertransference consists of thoughts and feelings that come from the therapist's personal history and arise from the patient's dynamics. The clinician is vulnerable to unconscious reactions that often arouse uncomfortable feelings. The patient's "badness" often provokes anger, which can be very disturbing. In interactional group work, the facilitator may see a patient as having "conned" the group. He or she may feel stunned when deceived and may have the urge to get even. This can provoke punitive reactions, particularly when a patient spews his or her anger on the facilitator.

It is difficult, at best, to know how to react constructively to patients' attacks. Nonetheless, the urge of the facilitator to retaliate, to seek revenge, is counterproductive, even when the client is being disrespectful. The facilitator must accept disrespect as normal client behavior, even though it is undesirable. Seeking revenge only solidifies the client's defenses and prevents the facilitator from being constructive; it binds the two together instead of freeing them. Expect some clients to attack you, even when there is no truth to their accusations; it is not the end of the world for you if they do. Hang in there with them; allow them to express their feelings without retaliation. Do not blame or attack clients; absorb their anguish, and let time help them resolve these transferences. Let them know you are with them, that you care about them, that you are there for them in spite of their hostility.

Basic Processes of Change in Interactional Group Counseling

This section discusses the processes that must occur for clients to benefit from interactional group counseling. These include dealing with resistance to here-and-now interaction, promoting positive group norms, and properly regulating control issues in the group.

Dealing With Resistance to the Here and Now and Acknowledging Anger

Initially, group members are very uncomfortable with the here and now; it is much safer to storytell about the past. They resist staying in the present and get very upset when they are given no topic or story to talk about. When they feel exposed in the present, group members attempt to force there-and-then talk. They are often unaware of how unsafe they feel.

I statements, instead of *we* statements, help the group stay in the here and now. Members are not accustomed to being so direct and to taking risks, however, so they strive to use *we, people, society,* and other general terms that afford more protection. They will likely show a great deal of resistance to using *I* and make constant attempts to use *we*. Once stripped of the protection afforded by the third person, however, the group will make use of *I* and *you* interactions. These interactions elicit many emotions, because the anonymity of the *we* is stripped away. At first, members fear that such emotions will be catastrophic for them and the group. Once they have learned to use the first person, though, they realize that they do not "dissolve" or "blow away." They come to appreciate a person's inner self, which results from here-and-now interactions. In addition, closeness develops, and group cohesion increases. When members come to support each other out of genuine feelings for each other, the group is working. Even so, you may have to enforce the *I* rule and encounter strong resistance in the process.

The here and now encourages clients to experience their feelings, including anger at other group members in the present. Clients with substance use disorders often have a high level of anger; they are accustomed to avoiding anger with alcohol and drugs and habitually isolate themselves. Anger provocation is high when group members attempt to confront each other in the here and now. Provoking others displaces the client's anger onto those others; it externalizes blame, and the client can then be a victim. By playing the victim, the client can disavow his or her anger. Typically, group members are not aware of their provocativeness, but the here-and-now setting of the group exposes this provocation and invites group members to respond. Expression of anger in the here and now allows members to take responsibility for their anger and thus gain more control over it. Here-and-now guidelines include encouraging members to talk directly to other group members, sharing and identifying with members, and giving positive and negative feedback as they struggle to stay in the present.

Promoting Positive Group Norms

Facilitators must observe and comment on group norms, the implicit and explicit rules that govern the operation of the group. A norm is a prescribed mode of behavior that guides a person's actions (D. W. Johnson & Johnson, 2006); therefore, norms influence group interaction. Most are implicit; they become accepted as a behavior everyone exhibits, even though the group does not explicitly and openly discuss the norm. Leaders can note a group's norms by watching the changes in the group's behavior that result from members' influence.

Members often feel a sense of norm ownership. Groups may adopt dysfunctional norms, such as using *we* instead of *I*. It may take direct facilitator influence to change this norm. In addition, norms often develop through indirect negotiation; these are called *implicit norms* (Kline, 2003). For example, a group may have an implicit norm to engage in competitive interactions. A strong group reaction to rule violation indicates the importance of a norm. When anger is not directly expressed in a group, the group likely has an implicit norm not to express anger; members need to work through this norm toward direct expression. Norms are difficult to change once they are solidified in a group. Obstructing norms include using *we* instead of *I*, adhering to the there and then, and interacting competitively. Helping norms include self-disclosing without fear, trusting others to act in one's best interest, sharing and exploring feelings, interacting in the here and now, checking for understanding, accepting negative feelings, openly addressing conflict, and discussing group process.

One absolutely mandatory group norm is that violence or the threat of violence must not be allowed. Clients with substance use disorders frequently believe that if they have justification for their anger, violence is an acceptable response. Violence and threats are never acceptable in the group; all members must remain physically safe.

Regulating Power and Control Issues in Group Process

Power and control issues are ever present in group sessions, but members pretend they are not. For that reason, the group leader must attend to these issues. Power is the capacity to effect outcomes (Forsyth, 1999). In a well-working group, the power is distributed among group members. When certain members exert power over a group, however, the situation must be confronted. For example, group members may draw attention to themselves and thus control the group, but they often deny that they need attention or that they hold control. Some members command attention but deny it and become angry when this is pointed out to them. A group becomes dysfunctional if a few members dominate it, because those members rescue the other participants by doing all the group's work. The quiet members can simply stay quiet, with no repercussions.

Clients with substance use disorders often have difficulty handling authority and control issues; some try to dominate, whereas others avoid confrontation by isolating themselves and drinking. Group members may say they cannot tell someone else what to do, but that may be exactly what they need to do. Of course, if they tell another person what to do, they open themselves up to being told what to do, and they do not want that. Other participants conform and never challenge authority. Ordering these members around until they rebel may be an effective strategy, because it often jars them loose. Just because of his or her title, members often respond to the facilitator with authority issues, sometimes "sucking up" and sometimes attacking. One member can even show both these behaviors over a short period of time, quickly vacillating from one to the other.

Groups often develop subgroups that keep secrets, which destabilizes the group and ties it in knots. Members believe secrets must be kept because, if released, these secrets will cause tremendous damage. Such behavior sets some members up to play the victim, harboring anger and resentment toward others; these feelings are never negotiated because they are kept hidden. In reality, the secret-keeping process is the true destructive force, because it ensures that not all members have a full deck of cards to play with. Clients with substance use disorders may want to conceal their drug use or the fact that they are HIV positive. Bringing secrets into the open in the group encourages closeness, caring, and support. It gives members an opportunity to grow and accept the truth. In the open, members must confront their rigid prejudices against one another. Protecting secrets is destructive, whereas supporting members to disclose allows for group movement.

Subgroups can also engage in triangulating, which occurs when two or more members gang up on another. The group needs to make public all subgroups and triangulation to empower the group to evaluate the effectiveness of such action. Blackmailing is another common process in groups. *Blackmailing* is a loose term, usually involving a threat to make members give the blackmailer what he or she wants. Evoking guilt can be a form of blackmailing, because it compels the victim to act on the blackmailer's behalf or else feel terrible. A bully blackmails by threatening bodily harm if the victim does not comply. Clients with substance use disorders are often good at blackmailing, demanding that other group members back down or back off. Blackmail is an unhealthy use of power, for it makes gains at another's expense and is intended to hurt others. It can be direct or subtle, but it must not be allowed to continue, because it will tie up the group, essentially holding the members hostage.

Blackmailing needs to be quickly recognized, brought out into the open of the group, and addressed directly, because it is a direct threat to the work and progress of the group. When confronted, members who are engaged in blackmail may deny it, yet directly challenging them often reduces blackmail. Above all, the blackmailer does not want to address his or her actions openly, for that will reduce the blackmail's power and threat. Do not let blackmail cripple your group. Because blackmail is often subtle, members need an "antenna" to detect it and bring it out in the open. It takes practice and experience to recognize the blackmail process, because it often occurs in an underground fashion.

Macho pride and its counterpart for women, the belief that men should be in charge and dominate women, lead to male subjugation of women in the group. Highlighting any male domination or sexual harassment gives the group an opportunity to address gender discrimination. Group process can bring out these issues for the group to explore, especially the sexual harassment of women. Macho pride is a basic issue, crippling relationships and leading to violent behavior; the group must not back away.

Most clients with substance use disorders avoid pain at all costs. Anger, macho pride, and rage are seen as acceptable for men, but in many male subcultures, acknowledging pain means one is less of a man. This is false. To feel one's pain is to accept oneself, others, and one's own limitations. This acceptance brings peace.

Pain expressed in group needs to be supported, not ridiculed. Those doing the ridiculing are uncomfortable with pain and want it to go away. Pain is not about feeling sorry for oneself; rather, it gives strength and the ability to move forward. Expressing pain and hurt in group fosters group cohesion and builds close member relationships. Nonetheless, members resist acknowledging pain, because it ties into issues of humiliation and shame. Clients with substance use disorders often avoid shame at all costs and certainly do not want to talk about it in a group, but admitting and sharing shame can be incredibly beneficial and therapeutic to the group. One member's pain may tap into that of others, for many have similar pain issues.

Clients often have great difficulty listening to others; many believe listening means giving up power or signifying agreement. They hear with their feelings, then interrupt and attack. Talking over others and not truly listening are common in groups. Although some members ramble on and need to be cut short, listening skills are strengthened through the group process. Clients often feel misunderstood, then trample on others' feelings when, in reality, what they saw as misunderstanding was just other members' lack of agreement. Participants need to learn to listen and then decide whether they disagree with others, which is respecting others rather than dismissing them.

Special Group Techniques

Observation of a group can be beneficial to both the group and the observer. An observer may be a group member, the group facilitator, or another clinician; he or she sits behind the group and listens without participating.

The group members may talk about the observer but cannot talk directly to him or her. No direct conversation can take place between the observer and group members, or the observer is no longer an observer but a group member. The role of the observer is to periodically offer a few short, distinct observations about group dynamics, including the leader's comments. For example, an observer may make brief, important points about group process, such as, "The group is very angry but has great difficulty expressing anger. In fact, the group is avoiding direct expression of anger at each other." Then the group returns to its business and may or may not address what the observer said.

Fishbowling takes place when one group observes another group in action and periodically offers comments. Again, the inner circle group cannot talk to the outer circle observers but can talk about them. Fishbowling is a powerful technique that provides plenty of opportunity for productive interactions. It may work well in a large substance abuse group that is divided into two subgroups, an inner and an outer circle. The outer circle observes and is periodically queried for a report to the group.

Role-plays of all kinds can be a valuable group experience, but because role-plays are usually directed by the facilitator, they reduce group interaction and increase interaction between the members and facilitator. With that said, role-plays can be most useful after the group has established a solid interaction among members, so the facilitator can become the center of focus, run the role-play, then retreat so the group members can interact with each other.

In the *hot-seat* technique, a group member talks to an empty chair, pretending that someone is sitting there in the here and now of the room. For example, a woman might imagine her mother is sitting in the empty chair. She speaks to her mother in the unfolding here and now, as if her mother is actually sitting in the chair at that moment. Then she may switch chairs and react by playing her mother. The participant is forced to confront her own projections. The technique helps the role-player to "own" these projections, because he or she is playing all the roles. Facilitators can alternate hot-seat work by having others play some of the roles, including "doubles"—that is, more than one person playing a single character. The goal of hot-seat work is not to resolve anything but to give group members the opportunity to take ownership of their projections and to encourage "percolation" of ideas—that is, to let the ideas work themselves out over time, not during the exercise.

While directing a hot-seat exercise, the facilitator may take on the role of a coach, director, referee, player, or alternate ego (i.e., playing a double in the empty chair). The technique is most useful when a client states that he or she has unfinished business with someone else, such as a parent. Clients may refuse to do hot-seat work because it is embarrassing or humiliating or because it makes them uncomfortable to act out a role; they may feel exposed, now that their private matter is public to the group.

The participant may need time to warm up, often by observing others in hot-seat work. The exercise can be powerful for the group as well; it often sparks issues in other members, and the group as a whole is moved to give support and encouragement.

Directing hot-seat work is an art form. The facilitator must create alternative forms of role-play, letting the action unfold as it happens and making it exciting, powerful, and attention grabbing for other group members. It takes time to develop expertise. Practice is the best way to develop one's skills as a hot-seat facilitator.

Groups can also exhibit *humor,* which members can easily participate in, understand, and sometimes own. Humor (not joke telling) is more acceptable than direct, negative, harsh confrontation. Laughing at oneself and at others' negative behavior can be supportive and builds group cohesion, and it is bonding behavior. Humor is helpful as long as it is not at another member's expense; for example, it can be used to expose a member's faulty beliefs in a good-natured way so he or she can accept them.

Personal mythology is how people see their place in the world; it is an expression of oneself, usually through a dream or story. Mythology is emotionally loaded; for example, a person's mythology might be how that person presents himself or herself to the outside world, so it involves looking good, not necessarily being good. For example, a narcissist sees himself or herself as the center of the universe and feels entitled to whatever he or she wants. In this mythology, others do not really matter; they are not even seen. In groups, members can be forced to confront their personal mythologies. They may avoid direct eye contact with other group members for fear of exposing their mythologies; thus, it is important that they learn to look directly at each other. Mythology gets tested and exposed through the engagement of other group members.

Kinds of Groups

Open-Ended and Closed-Ended Groups

Usually, counseling groups are either open ended or closed ended. Closed-ended groups start and end with the same members and may have a set number of sessions. Open-ended groups add new members when old members leave and have no ending date. Members come and go, but the group goes on. Existing members are not usually given a choice about who enters the group, because they would reject new members—they will likely find it very uncomfortable to add new members. At most substance abuse agencies, it is more practical to hold open-ended groups.

Stranger and Nonstranger Groups

Stranger groups consist of members who do not know each other and thus only see each other in the group sessions. Such groups are common in outpatient substance abuse clinics. Nonstranger groups are made up of members who do interact with each other outside of group—for example, groups drawn from a long-term inpatient setting, such as a therapeutic community. In nonstranger groups, the risk is far greater that members will be hurt and have to live with that hurt while continuing to meet with each other. Thus, issues of vulnerability, pride, humiliation, and shame are in the forefront in nonstranger groups, often prohibiting risk taking and self-disclosure.

Readings and Resources

Yalom, I. (2005). *The theory and practice of group psychotherapy* (5th ed.). New York: Basic Books.

> Yalom is a founding father of group psychotherapy. This book contains good discussions on transference and transparency, therapist training groups (i.e., T-groups; students can learn about small-group processes by participating in T-groups facilitated by an experienced practitioner), the value of the here and now, and resistance.

American Group Psychotherapy Association (www.groupsinc.org/).

> This organization is an interdisciplinary community that has been enhancing the practice, theory, and research of group therapy since 1942. It provides support for counselors to enhance their group leadership skills and holds a large annual group therapy education conference that is open to students.

Exercises

E.9.1. Observation of a Group

Observe one of the groups you are a part of, such as family or work. List some of the norms that operate in the group, both implicit and explicit. What rules prevent you from stating what you really feel toward some group members? If you were the facilitator of this group, how would you begin the session? Role-play this scenario, with one team member as the facilitator of the group.

E.9.2. Facilitating a Group

You are facilitating a substance abuse group. The members externalize and project blame onto you. How will you react to this blame? What will you do? How will you feel, and how will you manage your feelings? Role-play this scenario, with one team member as the facilitator of the group.

E.9.3. Group Role-Play: Setting Boundaries

You are running a group, and several members are missing or come late. What will you do to get the group to elicit commitment from the latecomer? How will you handle the group if they avoid the late person or condone lateness? How will you address the group when a member leaves to go to the bathroom? Role-play this scenario, with one team member as the facilitator of the group.

E.9.4. Role Play: Provacative Group Member

A group member is being extremely provocative toward you, goading you into an escalating conflict and trying to make you "the problem." How will you deal with this client; will you address him or her directly or get the group to confront the member? Explain. Role-play this scenario, with one team member as facilitator of the group.

The Role of the Substance Abuse Counselor in the Treatment of Clients With Both Substance Use Disorders and Mental Disorders

This chapter discusses the role substance abuse counselors can play in the treatment of clients with dual disorders. Topics include monitoring psychiatric symptoms, ensuring medication compliance and mental health treatment compliance, and educating the client about psychiatric symptoms as a trigger of substance abuse relapse. The chapter also gives an introduction to integrated treatment, an empirically supported approach for treating clients with substance abuse and severe mental illness. Harm reduction as a treatment goal is also discussed.

A large percentage of clients seeking treatment for substance use disorders have a mental disorder as well (Regier et al., 1990). Generally speaking, these clients have a more difficult time overcoming their problems than substance abusers without mental disorders. They tend to relapse, drop out of treatment, and fail to complete treatment more often (Mueser, Noordsy, Drake, & Fox, 2003). These clients require modifications to substance abuse treatment and attention to their mental disorders to achieve positive outcomes.

It is important to understand why such clients generally do not do as well as others in substance abuse treatment. Mental illness creates impairments in cognitive functioning and coping. For example, clients' symptoms can create problems with reality testing, the ability to distinguish between fantasies (e.g., dreams) and reality. People with mental illness tend to have impairments across the range of domains of social, self-care, and employment functioning, including parenting. This means that they have difficulties maintaining friendships, properly taking care of themselves, obtaining and maintaining employment, and providing good care for their children. The more impaired the client is by mental illness, the less able, generally speaking, he or she is to understand, remember, and implement the directions given in sessions.

People with mental illness can be divided into two broad categories: those with mild to moderate impairments, and those with severe impairments. People with severe impairments are considered seriously mentally ill. Diagnoses such as schizophrenia, bipolar disorder, and major depression can create such severe impairments.

Clients with serious mental illness (SMI) are generally treated in special clinics that focus on both the mental illness and the substance abuse problems. In the United States, these programs are typically part of the mental health system and are called dual diagnosis programs or mentally ill chemical abuse (MICA) programs. Patients with less severe impairments are seen in standard substance abuse programs and sometimes in the special programs mentioned above. Substance abuse counselors see some clients with both mental and substance use disorders in whatever context in which they work.

Traditionally, substance abuse counselors have not been responsible for treating clients' mental disorders because they have not received education and training in mental illness treatment. Conversely, other mental health professionals—including psychiatrists, psychologists, and social workers—who have the expertise to treat mental disorders typically are not trained to treat substance use disorders. In the past, this disconnect resulted in parallel treatment: The mental health professional treated the client for his or her mental illness, and the substance abuse counselor treated the client for his or her substance use disorder. The current model for treating SMI and substance use disorders is called integrated treatment, in which both disorders are treated by the same therapist or team of clinicians. Ideally, clinicians in these programs should be educated to understand and treat both kinds of disorders, but currently, this is not common. Drake, Bartels, Teague, Noordsy, and Clark (1993) have argued for the creation of a new professional group of specialists trained to treat both substance abuse and mental health disorders. Until this education and training issue is resolved, substance abuse counselors and other mental health professionals must work together to treat clients with dual disorders.

This chapter is only a brief introduction to the treatment of clients with substance use and mental disorders. Substance abuse counselors can benefit from additional education and training in mental health, especially if they work in dual diagnosis programs. Understanding psychiatric diagnosis, the role of medication, and the basics of mental health treatment is quite useful for counselors working in dual diagnosis programs.

The first part of the chapter discusses general issues pertaining to clients with both mental and substance use disorders. The second part deals with the specific issues of working with seriously mentally ill clients in dual diagnosis programs. Even though topics in the dual diagnosis section have particular relevance to clients with SMI treated in dual diagnosis programs, they also pertain to all substance abuse clients with mental disorders.

General Issues

Although substance abuse counselors do not have the expertise to treat mental illness, they can take some actions to help clients manage and cope with their mental illness. It is first important to determine whether clients have a mental disorder, because it affects the treatment. In dual diagnosis programs, diagnosis is routinely handled by staff psychiatrists or other mental health professionals.

In conventional substance abuse programs, counselors often have the responsibility of determining whether clients should be evaluated for mental illness. Clients who have symptoms of depression, anxiety, or an unusual manner of relating or speaking may have an underlying mental illness. Counselors should refer clients with such symptoms or any client they think might have a mental disorder for a psychiatric consultation.

PTSD, depressive disorders, and personality disorders commonly co-occur with substance use disorders; clients with these disorders (often undiagnosed) are frequently treated in conventional substance abuse programs. Although these clients are often less impaired than those with SMI, they need treatment modifications to achieve good outcomes.

As the substance abuse counselor, you can help treat a comorbid mental disorder by monitoring its symptoms, paying attention to medication and mental health treatment compliance, discussing the relationship between the client's psychiatric symptoms and his or her substance use, and developing commonsense goals for the client. Discussions of the psychiatric diagnosis are better left to the psychiatrist or other mental health clinician.

Monitoring Medication Compliance

Powerful medications exist that can alleviate many of the symptoms of psychiatric illness. Most of these medications, however, must be taken indefinitely. They do not cure the illness. Therefore, it is important that the client take the medications. In many instances, the substance abuse counselor is the person at the clinic who has the most contact with the client. Thus, the counselor has the best opportunity to monitor medication compliance.

In each session, therefore, it is important to determine whether clients are taking their medication as prescribed. If they are, they should be praised. Suggest that this compliance has contributed to clinical improvements you have seen (Center for Substance Abuse Treatment, 2000a). If they have not been taking their medication as prescribed, discuss the reasons they have discontinued or altered the dose or frequency.

For example, some clients may become discouraged and stop taking the medication because it may take several weeks to have a therapeutic effect. Consult with the psychiatrist to find out whether the prescribed medication takes time to have an effect, and, if this is the case, educate the patient (Center for Substance Abuse Treatment, 2000a). If specific side effects are bothering clients, the psychiatrist may be able to lower the dose or change the medication to one that does not have the side effects but still treats the psychiatric symptoms.

You should review with clients any possible interaction effects between the medication they are taking and nonprescribed drugs and alcohol. Discuss with clients their specific drugs of choice and the drugs' effects on the prescribed medication. Alcohol and street drugs may negate a medication's therapeutic effects, or they may intensify the medication's psychoactive effect and cause an overdose reaction. Should clients who relapse into heavy alcohol or drug use continue to take prescribed medication? Although there is some danger of interactions between the drugs, given the balance between the dangers of the interactions with the dangers of relapsing in both mental illness and substance use disorders, it is probably better to advise clients to continue to take the medications and see the psychiatrist (Mueser et al., 2003). They should, of course, be evaluated for detoxification.

Counselors should consider the following questions when clients are not compliant with their medication:

- Does the client understand the benefits of taking the medication?
- Are there bothersome side effects that need to be addressed?
- Does the client misattribute problems to the medications which are due to other causes?
- Is the client afraid of interactions with alcohol/drugs and the medications?
- Does the client need help to overcome forgetfulness?
- Can the regimen easily fit into [the] client's routine?
- Is the regimen unnecessarily complicated? (Mueser et al., 2003, p. 296)

When the reasons for the noncompliance are discovered, they can be problem solved with the client and the collaboration of the psychiatrist.

Monitoring and Supporting Mental Health Treatment

In addition to medication, specific empirically validated cognitive–behavioral interventions have been developed for many psychiatric disorders. These therapies are often just as effective as medication for some disorders (e.g., anxiety disorders, depression) and can be combined with medication. When such treatment is provided to clients, the counselor should monitor attendance, support the client's involvement, problem solve issues that may arise, and be sure that the substance abuse treatment provided is in concert with the specialized mental health treatment.

Helping Clients Become Aware of Symptoms That Affect Their Substance Use

In many cases, when clients have dual disorders, their psychiatric symptoms are associated with their substance use and can contribute to relapses into substance abuse. Thus, it is important to become familiar with clients' psychiatric symptoms and explore with clients how these symptoms interact with their substance use problems (e.g., using drugs or alcohol to cope with symptoms, to facilitate social relationships, or to escape boredom or depression).

Monitoring Symptoms of the Psychiatric Disorder

Although substance abuse counselors do not have the training to diagnose psychiatric disorders, they can notice when clients begin to have psychiatric symptoms or their functioning deteriorates. For example, if a client reports isolating more and more and stops going to scheduled activities, this should be taken as a warning sign. The counselor can discuss this behavior with the client in a commonsense manner but should also refer the client to the psychiatrist for evaluation of a possible relapse into mental illness. If clients begin to focus on their psychiatric concerns, they may be experiencing more severe psychiatric symptoms. If you think this is likely, you should ensure that the client receives immediate psychiatric attention. Many such clients, those with SMI in particular, are periodically in crisis, irrational, delusional, incoherent, or paranoid or show other severe psychiatric symptoms. When this occurs, they should be given psychiatric care immediately. The example dialogue below, which takes place at the beginning of a session, illustrates in brief how to make this intervention.

Counselor: How have you been since last session?
Client: [unshaven, disheveled, seems distraught] Are you trying to hurt me?
Counselor: No. You seem to be upset today.
Client: Someone is trying to hurt me. I will have to stay here all night. They can come through the walls to get me.
Counselor: I can see you don't feel safe today. Dr. Shepherd can help you with this problem better than I can. Let's go over to see him.

In sessions with your clients, you should allow them to talk about their psychiatric concerns, but if you do not know how to help, you can say so. It is true that some clients may avoid talking about their addictive behavior by talking about their other problems. This is where prioritizing (discussed in Chapter 3) comes in. You need to ask yourself, "Is this really the main issue the client needs to deal with today?" Sometimes it will be; severe depression trumps a discussion of how many AA or NA meetings the client will attend next week. As mentioned above, when clients talk about their psychiatric symptoms, this may indicate concerns they have about their psychiatric illness and could signal a possible relapse. In this case, referral to the psychiatrist is appropriate. Alternatively, if a client is just venting about his or her landlord, for example, you can say, "How can I help you with this problem?" If, after some discussion, if you believe the client is avoiding talking about his or her substance abuse, you can say, "I can see this is important to you, but we are approaching the end of the hour, and we need to talk about your cocaine use."

Clients with dual disorders sometimes make irrational and unrealistic statements. It is not helpful to confront these statements. Counselors can provide gentle redirection rather than confrontation when the client expresses an unrealistic thought. For example, as a client walks in, he or she might say, "You are against me today, I feel it." The counselor could say, "Gee, I don't think so. What's been happening since our last session?" By saying this, the counselor gently disagrees and then seeks to find out whether some incident has affected the client. There is nothing to be gained by challenging the client and everything to be lost.

Developing Commonsense Goals

Counselors can offer commonsense advice to alleviate clients' symptoms. For example, if the client is depressed, the counselor can encourage him or her to get out of the house before noon and follow a physical exercise plan. Often, clients with a dual diagnosis are so distracted by their symptoms that they have difficulty problem solving issues that arise; in many cases, counselors can help.

Integrated Treatment for the Seriously Mentally Ill and Substance-Abusing Client

Special programs have been created to treat clients with SMI and substance abuse disorders. The primary treatment philosophy for such programs is called integrated treatment. The principles of integrated treatment include

- integration of services,
- comprehensiveness of services offered,
- assertiveness in outreach to clients,
- commitment to reduction of negative consequences of the mental illness and substance abuse as the treatment goal (harm reduction),
- long-term perspective for treatment to effect change,
- motivation-based treatment (incorporates principles of MI), and
- multiple psychotherapeutic modalities.

For many clients, partial remission of symptoms is most common, rather than complete remission of symptoms (Mueser et al., 2003).

Integrated treatment has its own sequence of treatment stages:

1. *Engagement:* The treatment goal of this stage is involving the client in treatment.
2. *Persuasion:* The treatment goal of this stage is developing the client's motivation for addressing the substance abuse problem (i.e., use of modified MI).
3. *Active treatment:* The treatment goal of this stage is helping the client change his or her addictive behavior.
4. *Relapse prevention:* The treatment goal of this stage is helping the client maintain the positive changes he or she has made.

These stages are similar in many respects to the stages of change discussed in Chapter 2. Much like the stages of change, each stage has preferred strategies and techniques to achieve the therapeutic goals of the stage. The main difference is integrated therapy's engagement stage, which can be seen as a stage before precontemplation in the Stages of Change Model. In engagement, the goal is simply to motivate the client to get involved in treatment. Counselors often do not even raise substance abuse issues during this phase. From the MI perspective, in this stage, the counselor is developing rapport through empathy.

Working as Part of a Team

Staffing in dual diagnosis programs is multidisciplinary, including psychiatrists, nurses, psychologists or social workers, case managers, and substance abuse counselors. Ideally, all staff are trained in mental health and addiction. In many programs, however, treatment teams are blended with substance abuse and other mental health professionals. Ideally, staff receive on-the-job training that lasts about a year to teach them the principles of integrated treatment.

In dual diagnosis programs, the different kinds of professionals provide specific interventions based on their training. Psychiatrists diagnose, evaluate, and monitor medication. Psychologists and social workers provide therapy for mental disorders, including treatment for PTSD, childhood sexual abuse, anxiety, depression, and personality disorders. Psychiatric nurses administer medication. Case managers work with clients who are severely impaired and coordinate their care and treatment. The substance abuse counselor is an important part of this team, providing the main interventions for substance use disorders. One of the challenges you will have if you work in such a program is learning how to collaborate with your colleagues. You must advocate for your client, learn to compromise, remain respectful of your colleagues, and defer to the appropriate professional for clinical concerns when you do not have the necessary expertise.

Elements of Dual Diagnosis Programs

Dual diagnosis programs treat clients' mental illness. This treatment includes an assessment of the mental illness, evaluation for medication, provision of medication, and other therapy for the mental illness, such as CBT. The goal is to stabilize the patient so that his or her psychiatric symptoms go into remission and do not interfere with his or her functioning.

The treatment addresses the addictive disorder as well. Treatment for clients with dual diagnosis takes a gradual, step-by-step approach to engage the client, raise his or her awareness of the substance abuse problem, seek his or her cooperation and build motivation, and help him or her change. (See the stages of treatment listed above.) This approach specifically incorporates MI. It also includes medications that are helpful in substance use reduction, harm reduction goals, and self-help involvement. Dual diagnosis programs provide groups focused on addiction issues depending on the client's motivational level. They offer a number of interventions to help the family understand, cope with, and help the client with SMI.

Case management is the central clinical intervention for the community treatment of clients with dual disorders (Mueser et al., 2003, p. 87). As a substance abuse counselor, you may be hired as a case manager. If so, you must seek information and training about mental illness, because the standard substance abuse training curriculum does not include sufficient education and training on mental illness. You need to understand psychiatric diagnosis, the role of medication in the treatment of mental illness, the current conception of the treatment and outcome of mental illness, and basic supportive interventions for mentally ill clients. At a minimum, you need to take a course on abnormal psychology, a course on counseling in mental illness, and, ideally, a course on dual diagnosis and case management. This chapter does not provide sufficient information and education for this purpose.

Case managers are responsible for coordinating care of the dually diagnosed client. Additionally, because these clients are severely impaired, they need help managing their lives. The case manager helps the client make medical and other necessary appointments; ensures that he or she attends them; and makes sure the client follows through on treatment recommendations and mandated requirements, by closely monitoring medication compliance and the results of drug and alcohol tests. The case manager also helps the client handle the crises that often arise.

Case managers may conduct outreach into the community to engage potential clients. This nontraditional task demands skills not typically taught in conventional mental health or substance abuse counseling programs. In this stage of treatment, the goals are to provide practical help to the client so that he or she will develop trust in the counselor and become involved in the treatment program.

As the client becomes engaged in treatment, the case manager coordinates the care, making sure that a complete assessment is done and medication is prescribed, obtained, and taken. Substance abuse issues are introduced slowly, in a stepwise sequence. Eventually, the client has the opportunity to focus on his or her substance use and work on cutting down use or on abstinence. In the meantime, harm reduction (see the discussion below) is the interim goal for the client. All treatment interventions must be coordinated and monitored by the case manager. It is the case manager's responsibility to promote follow-through on all aspects of the treatment plan. When clients fail to follow through, as they often do, the case manager tries to understand why and resolve the problem (Mueser et al., 2003, p. 96).

Another important responsibility of the case manager is advocating for the client. The case manager assists clients in obtaining such basic needs as food and clothing (Mueser et al., 2003, p. 97) and is responsible for ensuring that clients gain access to treatment programs, receive entitlements, have housing, are given appropriate legal representation for legal proceedings, and receive appropriate medical care. Case management is clearly a demanding and intensive job! In addition to being case managers in dual diagnosis programs, substance abuse counselors may run substance abuse groups at the motivational, action stage, and relapse prevention levels; serve as self-help liaisons for clients; provide individual substance abuse counseling; and offer psychoeducation about substance use disorders and related topics to clients and their families.

Modifications to MI for Dual Diagnosis Clients

One way to think about many of the integrated treatment strategies discussed above is that this approach slows down the MI process to fit the more limited capacities of clients with SMI. The principles and goals of MI remain largely intact, however.

The biggest difference comes in the first phase of treatment, engagement, which is not a part of MI. From the MI perspective, in this stage, the counselor uses empathy to develop rapport. Martino, Carroll, Kostas, Perkins, and Rounsaville (2002) made the following recommendations for counselors to engage severely mentally ill clients in treatment:

- Providing support, showing a nonjudgmental attitude, and using listening skills are important strategies to facilitate engagement.
- Sharing one's personal experience with overcoming addiction or other problems may be useful at this stage.
- Engaging in more general discussions about nonclinical topics may be helpful when one is trying to build rapport, so that the client can be reminded that he or she is viewed as a human being despite having an addiction.
- Confrontation is de-emphasized, and motivational enhancement is emphasized.

Martino et al. (2002) published additional modifications to MI for treating dually diagnosed clients. They recommended that counselors phrase open questions in a simple manner. For example, to learn about the effect of alcohol and drugs on the client's psychiatric symptoms, it is better to ask how alcohol or the specific drug affects the symptoms the client has. If one of the client's symptoms is depression and he or she drinks alcohol, you can ask, "How does the alcohol affect your depression?" This is a simple request that is easy for the client to understand and respond to. Alternatively, "How do alcohol and other drugs affect your psychiatric symptoms?" is fairly complicated and abstract. It is better to keep your questions simple and ask follow-up questions if necessary.

Reflections also need to be modified to fit the capacities of the client. Reflections should be simple and phrased in concise language—you should make use of metaphors; avoid excessive focus on despair, bad events, and negative things; and be sure to give patients enough time to respond to reflections you have made (Martino et al., 2002). Use reflection and summaries often to help structure the interview and maintain a logical organization to the conversation. The following dialogue is an example of how to modify reflections for severely mentally ill clients:

> *Client:* What's wrong with me is that my mind and body go in old directions any time I confront new situations of substance use with people.
> *Therapist:* You find yourself using again when people who use drugs are around you.
> *Client:* Yeah, like I wasn't planning on it, but it was put before me somehow, like they are setting me up again.
> *Therapist:* Your intention is not to use drugs, but it is hard not to use when you are around people who do.
> *Client:* I can't say I don't try to use. But these people are evil, bad. I know what they are thinking. But they won't get the best of me.
> *Therapist:* They are of no help to you, and you really want to stay away from them to be the best you can be without using drugs.
> *Client:* That's right. (Martino et al., 2002, p. 304)

The following example dialogue shows how to avoid repeating the client's despairing statements:

> *Client:* You know, I was hit a lot by my mother growing up. Sometimes she was a vicious angry woman—very strict. I remember she slapped me so hard I heard my brains rattle. "Don't hit me again," my mind would say, "or I'll hit you back." Now I'm told to hit back if I'm not being treated right.
> *Therapist:* Told to hit back.
> *Client:* I hear voices that tell me to hit people when I don't like them.
> *Therapist:* Then what happens?

Client: I try not to do it. You know, my brother used to treat me badly, too. That son of a bi—

Therapist: So even though many people have treated you badly, you don't want to hurt others.

Client: That's usually when I get high.

Therapist: Getting high helps you not do what the voices are telling you to do.

Client: In the moment but then it messes up my mind more.

Therapist: So getting high is good in the moment, but over the long haul it makes matters worse for you. (Martino et al., 2002, p. 304)

Martino et al. (2002) argued that the MI principle of giving positive feedback is even more important for clients with SMI than for less-impaired clients, to encourage a good collaborative relationship. Another fundamental principle stressed by MI is feeling and expressing empathy for the client. This may be difficult with some severely mentally ill clients. They can be dependent, unrealistic, irrational, inconsistent, and subject to disturbing symptoms, such as hallucinations. To increase your empathy for these clients, consider that they are subject to anxiety and fears you probably have never experienced. Many psychotic symptoms are terrifying. Clients with SMI often feel very bad about themselves because of their symptoms and their problems coping and functioning. Some cannot even trust their own thoughts or feelings. Imagine what that would be like. Consider what it must be like to navigate the world without really understanding it or feeling understood. Often, clients with SMI feel that they are carrying extra burdens that the average person does not have to deal with. You should also consider how the stigma attached to mental illness affects these clients. It is important to look at your own feelings about people who have dual disorders to be sure that you can provide appropriate empathy.

Harm Reduction and Realistic Goals

The text has emphasized having patience and setting step-by-step, modest goals for clients with substance use disorders. These considerations are even more important with dual diagnosis clients. *Harm reduction* refers to more modest goals of treatment for substance use disorders than in traditional substance abuse treatment, in which the goal is abstinence from all psychoactive substances. As the term implies, the goal of harm reduction is to reduce the harm the client faces in his or her life. This means that the client can be taught to decrease his or her consumption of harmful drugs or to use drugs in a safer manner so that he or she is at less risk for contracting diseases such as HIV and hepatitis C, injuring himself or herself and others, or becoming a victim of a crime. The harm reduction approach makes sense for many clients who suffer from dual disorders, especially at the beginning of treatment. It is difficult to engage these clients with the goal of abstinence. An emphasis on harm reduction makes it easier to develop a working relationship with the client, to address the most devastating effects of substance use, and to harness the client's motivation for sobriety over the long term. Many clients with SMI do eventually endorse abstinence from substance use and even achieve it, but not as the initial goal (K. T. Mueser, personal communication, July 2008).

An additional problem for clients with a dual diagnosis is that a relapse in their mental illness may lead to a relapse in their use of substances, and vice versa. For many clients, the best outcome a counselor can provide is periods of remission from the disorders, rather than stable remission. Thus, counselors must work hard to keep their goals realistic and not allow themselves to become disappointed when clients relapse, as they often do. These relapses can create crises and require proactive intervention to protect the client and his or her family, another form of harm reduction.

Dual diagnosis programs often have their own protocols for treatment interventions. Your supervisor will help you learn them and provide guidance on implementation.

Modified Substance Abuse Treatment for Clients With Co-Occurring PTSD

PTSD commonly co-occurs with substance abuse disorders (Kessler et al., 1997). Clients who have a substance use disorder and this co-occurring condition are sometimes treated in dual diagnosis programs but often are served in traditional substance abuse treatment programs. Although they are typically less impaired than clients with SMI, these patients need modifications to standard substance abuse treatment. Recommended modifications include the following:

- medication for the psychiatric symptoms;
- harm reduction goals rather than abstinence, especially at the beginning of treatment;
- provision for relapse, which may be triggered by PTSD symptoms;
- concurrent psychotherapy for the PTSD;
- psychoeducation about the relationship between the two disorders; and
- family counseling, if family members are supportive of recovery. (Yalisove, 2004)

Readings and Resources

Center for Substance Abuse Treatment. (1998). *Comprehensive case management for substance abuse treatment* (Treatment Improvement Protocol Series 27, DHHS Publication No. SMA 98-3222). Rockville, MD: Substance Abuse and Mental Health Services Administration.

This volume provides a good introduction to case management in substance abuse treatment. It includes a section on substance abuse clients with mental illness.

Center for Substance Abuse Treatment. (2005). *Substance abuse treatment for persons with co-occurring disorders* (Treatment Improvement Protocol Series 42, DHHS Publication No. SMA 05-3922). Rockville, MD: Substance Abuse and Mental Health Services Administration.

Chapters 4 and 5 provide good guidance for treating co-occurring disorders.

Denning, P., Little, J., & Glickman, A. (2004). *Over the influence: The harm reduction guide for managing drugs and alcohol.* New York: Guilford Press.

This book provides a good introduction to the harm reduction point of view.

Mueser, K. T., Noordsy, D. L., Drake, R. E., & Fox, L. (2003). *Integrated treatment for dual disorders.* New York: Guilford Press.

This book is a good guide for understanding the integrated treatment model.

Najavits, L. M. (2002). *Seeking safety: A treatment manual for PTSD and substance abuse.* New York: Guilford Press.

This book presents a treatment approach for treating clients with substance use disorders and PTSD.

Tatarsky, A. (Ed.). (2002). *Harm reduction psychotherapy.* Northvale, NJ: Jason Aronson.

This book includes several case studies describing the treatment of patients with substance use and mental disorders.

Yalisove, D. L. (2004). *Introduction to alcohol research.* Boston: Allyn & Bacon.

Chapter 10 gives a good introduction to some basic dual diagnosis treatment concepts, such as the *DSM–IV–TR* diagnostic criteria and the relationship between mental disorders and substance use disorders.

Information on harm reduction can be found at the Harm Reduction Coalition's Web site: www.harmreduction.org.

Exercises

E.10.1. Person With SMI

Imagine or observe a person with SMI. Can you imagine the world that person lives in? Can you sense his or her anxieties, fears, and depression? Do you see how he or she is stigmatized? Write down your reactions to this person, and discuss whether empathy is difficult or easy and why. This will be a part of the workbook log.

E.10.2. Your Personal Feelings About Mental Illness

Discuss your personal feelings about mental illness and whether you have any negative feelings about mentally ill people. How might these feelings affect your ability to provide counseling for such clients? This will be a part of the workbook log.

E.10.3. Role-Play: Engaging Client With Mental Illness

One team member role-plays a homeless person with mental illness and a drinking problem who is in the engagement stage (i.e., not yet motivated for treatment or aware of an addiction problem) and who is interested in having a place to stay. Another team member plays a counselor trying to engage him or her in treatment. This will be a part of the workbook log. Be sure that the observers keep a detailed record of the dialogue. Remember to set goals and techniques before beginning the role-play.

E.10.4. Role-Play: Client With Bipolar Disorder

One team member plays a client with bipolar disorder who is still using crack cocaine, although she has been coming regularly to sessions. She has lost custody of her child and would like to regain custody. Another team member plays a counselor trying to help the client examine the pros and cons of using crack cocaine. This will be a part of the workbook log. Be sure that the observers keep a detailed record of the dialogue. Remember to set goals and techniques before beginning the role-play.

E.10.5. Role-Play: Client With Schizophrenia

One team member plays a client with schizophrenia and alcohol abuse who states that he or she has to drink whenever he or she becomes anxious and does not know how else to deal with these feelings. Another team member role-plays a counselor trying to teach the client to use self-talk or other skills to deal with anxiety. This will be a part of the workbook log. Be sure that the observers keep a detailed record of the dialogue. Remember to set goals and techniques before beginning the role-play.

E.10.6. Role-Play: Client With PTSD

One team member role-plays a client with PTSD and cannabis abuse who has just begun medication for depression. Another team member role-plays the substance abuse counselor asking about treatment compliance and effects of the medication. This will be a part of the workbook log. Be sure that the observers keep a detailed record of the dialogue. Remember to set goals and techniques before beginning the role-play.

E.10.7. Role-Play: Client Exhibiting Psychiatric Symptoms

One team member role-plays a client with SMI who is beginning to show psychiatric symptoms (depression, agitation, etc.; the team can decide which symptoms) and who acknowledges that he or she is not taking his or her medication. A second team member role-plays the counselor who problem solves the noncompliance. This will be a part of the workbook log. Be sure that the observers keep a detailed record of the dialogue. Remember to set goals and techniques before beginning the role-play.

Chapter 11

Working With the Significant Others of Clients With Substance Use Disorders

Errol O. Rodriguez

Current estimates suggest that approximately 18 million Americans struggle with alcohol abuse and dependence and 4 million suffer from a substance use disorder (Straussner, 2003). One in four deaths in America can be attributed to the effects of alcohol, tobacco, or illicit substances, and as many as 75% of domestic violence victims report that their abuser was drinking alcohol or using illicit substances at the time of the assault (Johns Hopkins University, 2008). Given the commonly accepted formula for measuring the effect of a person with a substance use disorder on another person, it is estimated that up to six people are affected by one person with a substance use disorder. In other words, approximately 92.7 to 139.1 million Americans are frequently affected by someone's substance use disorder (McIntyre, 1993).

Consequently, it is not surprising that people who live with or care for someone with a substance use disorder experience significant emotional distress and trauma. Given the chronic nature of substance use disorders, these caregivers or concerned significant others (CSOs) are at risk for developing maladaptive ways of coping with their experiences, which often translates into complex psychological and behavioral patterns of interacting with the substance-using person. In addition, CSOs may experience resentment, anger, hopelessness, powerlessness, anxiety, and depression as a result of the emotional challenges of trying to persuade a loved one with a substance use disorder to accept help for his or her use.

For years, counselors have struggled to understand the impact of substance use on significant others. During the 1930s, many psychologists believed that the female partners of alcoholic men had disturbed personalities and resolved their inner conflicts through their relationships to alcoholic men. In fact, Whalen (1953) created psychological profiles of women who were married to alcoholic men. He asserted that these profiles captured the women's underlying conflict. "Punitive Polly" had issues with her aggression, "Controlling Catherine" was controlling, "Suffering Susan" experienced some satisfaction from her masochistic ways of interacting with her alcoholic husband, and "Wavering Winifred" struggled with a significant degree of ambivalence about her husband's alcoholism. According to Whalen's theory, women married to alcoholic men obtained secondary gains from their spouse, whose substance use disorder provided the women a vehicle to work through their own neurotic conflicts.

Not until the mid-1950s did a shift occur in clinical thinking about family members of alcoholics. Pioneered by several researchers and clinicians (Cork, 1969; Jackson, 1954; Kellerman, 1969; Steinglass, Davis, & Berenson, 1977), a more useful framework emerged for assisting partners and family members of people with substance use disorders. Over the course of the following decades, clinicians and researchers recognized that the psychological problems of CSOs were not necessarily the result of a pre-existing personality disturbance. Rather, CSOs developed psychological problems as a result of caring for loved ones with substance use disorders and the often progressive nature of the disorder (Rodriguez, 2005).

Today, counselors use an array of interventions to treat patients with substance use disorders and their families. Nonetheless, despite the years of research and clinical wisdom, counselors continue to find it difficult to engage CSOs over the long term. The remainder of this chapter focuses on skills, techniques, and strategies you can use to engage and begin work with CSOs in clinical treatment.

Principles for Working With Concerned Significant Others

The primary principles for working with CSOs are expressing empathy, working with ambivalence, and constructively engaging resistance. Additionally, the principles of Community Reinforcement and Family Training (CRAFT), systems theory, and self-care are also important.

Treatment Duration and Goals of Treatment

The duration of treatment for CSOs is generally brief (e.g., up to 16 sessions). Given the nature of substance abuse counseling and the potential for other issues that need attention (e.g., domestic violence and medical, vocational, and legal problems), however, the counselor should not set a limit to treatment in advance. This kind of intervention has three overall goals:

1. to alleviate the suffering and reduce the maladaptive behavior of the CSO and to facilitate the recovery of the significant other with a substance use disorder (SUD SO) by changing the interactions between the CSO and SUD SO,

2. to help the CSO develop self-care attitudes and behavior, and
3. to get the SUD SO to accept treatment for his or her substance use disorder.

The following three goals serve as a guide in all session work:

1. Establish and maintain rapport,
2. determine what is the most important task to accomplish in each session, and
3. select strategies to use to reduce the CSO's distress and promote change in the relationship dyad.

Establishing and maintaining rapport are essential goals in any counseling relationship. Rapport sets the stage for the use of interventions and all the therapeutic work that follows. Additionally, the counselor needs to determine what task is most important to accomplish in each session. This is often done on a hunch, on the basis of the initial conversation in each session. The CSO might begin the session by stating that his or her spouse drank alcohol last night and became physically abusive. This information requires the counselor to inquire about safety and personal injury, which becomes an important task of the session. In another session, the CSO might share that he or she feels sad and has been having difficulty sleeping. In this case, the counselor needs to ask follow-up questions to assess for depression. In other words, the counselor uses the beginning of each session to get a sense of what the CSO needs and to choose strategies to help reduce the CSO's distress and potentially foster insight about the CSO's own experience and reactions to the SUD SO. Remember, an important goal in working with CSOs in general is to increase the likelihood that they will return for the next session.

The Initial Contact

In most cases, CSOs seek help before their SUD SO does. In general, CSOs have experienced a long sequence of events with the SUD SO that has led to their willingness to reach out for help. Therefore, the overall goal of the initial contact is to help the client feel comfortable about seeking help. During the initial contact and subsequent sessions, you must remain aware of a few key issues:

1. The CSO is in distress.
2. CSOs' own behavior may affect the SUD SO; CSOs are often unaware that their reactions to their SUD SO can influence his or her decision to use or not use.
3. You need to assess the potential for violence or endangerment, which may negatively affect treatment.

To address these issues, you will need to listen empathically, demonstrate an understanding of the CSO's current distress, maintain a nonjudgmental stance, and instill hope.

Carl Rogers (1992), perhaps more than any other figure in psychology, emphasized the use of empathy in the therapeutic relationship to bring about change in personality and behavior. According to Rogers (1992), to achieve an empathic understanding, counselors need to experience the private world of the patient as if it were their own, without becoming entangled in it. In other words, a counselor may experience feelings and reactions similar to those expressed by the CSO. To demonstrate such understanding, counselors may simply reflect back to the CSO their sense of the salient issues as well as issues that the CSO may be scarcely aware of. For example, if a woman reports that her husband drinks all the time and does not come home when he is on a binge, you might say, "His drinking and not coming home must be scary and upsetting for you." This simple, reflective comment lets the woman know that she has been heard and that you are attuned to her feelings.

Because many CSOs report a range of feelings, such as anger, resentment, confusion, depression, and anxiety, it is important to listen for them. Some CSOs report these feelings easily, as the emotions are right on the surface of awareness. Others, however, report them less easily and need the counselor's help to articulate them. For example, a man expresses that his wife continues to drink despite her health problems and that their arguments about her drinking are affecting their children. As he is discussing these issues, he begins to cry and hit the table. You might say, "It is really hard to watch someone you care about hurt herself and to witness how it affects your children. I can understand feeling very sad and angry."

In another example, a wife expresses great concern about her husband's cocaine and alcohol use and his lying and manipulation. In the same breath, however, she also says that he is a good man and a great father and that maybe she is seeing his behavior as more of a problem than it actually is. She seems to be confused, sad, and scared, especially when she thinks about what will happen to her family if her husband does not stop using drugs. You might say, "It is scary to think about losing your family, and it sounds like you go back and forth on what to do about it, perhaps because of the pain you anticipate feeling if you fully acknowledge the degree of his use and behavior. However, you did take a big step today by reaching out for help."

In this example, you recognize the client's emotional distress, ambivalence, denial, and minimization and support her decision for change. You will encounter ambivalence in your work with CSOs, because most significant others struggle with their feelings about their loved one's behavior. Understanding ambivalence as a natural response to uncertainty and the difficulty of making critical decisions is essential in work with CSOs. It is wise to accept their ambivalence and roll with their resistance—that is, instead of confronting their denial of their problem or their minimization of it, simply acknowledge how hard it is to make a critical change in one's life, and support their decision to ask for help. (See Chapter 2 for a discussion of ambivalence.)

When you are assessing and working with CSOs' ambivalence, it is equally important to consider their awareness of their own behavior and their willingness to change it. CSOs generally seek counseling services to change the SUD SO and less frequently to change themselves. Therefore, the counselor needs to discuss the relevance of self-change and its significance in helping the loved one achieve abstinence. The counselor might say, "You have taken a big step to ask for help for your loved one, but helping him change his behavior is often best accomplished when you are willing to look honestly at yourself and make some changes as well."

Most CSOs respond positively to such comments and state their willingness to self-examine in an effort to help their loved one. To further assess a CSO's willingness to self-examine, you might say, "What are some things that you would like to change about yourself that may also have a positive influence on your loved one?" CSOs commonly state that they would like to stop yelling at the SUD SO, stop being so easily manipulated by him or her, or become more independent of him or her. These and other, similar statements indicate the CSO's willingness to look at his or her own needs and behavior and are important elements in counseling work based on CRAFT strategies, which are discussed later in this chapter.

Additionally, during the initial contact, the counselor should focus on instilling hope. Many CSOs enter the counseling relationship with a moderate degree of motivation sufficient to start the change process, but, over time, their motivation and commitment often wane. To instill hope and capitalize on the client's current motivation, you can share your familiarity with the CSO's problems by describing previous experiences with other CSOs in general terms. This may give the CSO increased confidence in your ability to help him or her, and it provides a feeling of universality—that is, the sense that the CSO is not alone with his or her problem and that many others have found themselves in similar difficult circumstances. For example, you might say, "I have counseled many people with very similar circumstances who were scared, angry, and hurt by the behavior of their loved one with a substance use disorder. I have also seen the positive changes that can occur from a counseling intervention for the family." The instillation of hope and expression of universality are important components in most therapeutic strategies but are clearly essential for clients affected by a SUD SO.

During the initial contact, counselors also need to assess the potential for violence or other signs of endangerment. Some of the strategies used in counseling may trigger negative reactions from the SUD SO. Therefore, it is crucial that the counselor explore any potential for harm to the CSO or other members of the family. A key predictor in assessing violence is any history of violence. Accordingly, you might say, "Have there been any situations in which you have felt physically afraid of your spouse? Is there anyone other than you—such as your child or an older adult—who is in danger of harm by your spouse?"

CSOs may feel uncomfortable talking about violence or victimization. It is very important to remain sensitive and patient when exploring the potential for violence. Pay particular attention to any physical signs of injury, reports of significant anxiety or depression, and reports of isolation from friends or family.

The counselor may also use the Conflict Tactics Scales (Straus, Hamby, & McCoy, 1996), an assessment tool that measures the extent to which intimate partners engage in psychological and physical abuse and their ability to negotiate such conflicts. The CSO's answers to general questions about partner violence and his or her responses to items on the Conflict Tactics Scales will help you decide whether to proceed with treatment or pursue a plan for safety. Safety always takes priority. If you determine that the client is at a high risk for violence or if he or she has reported violence, you must develop an immediate plan for safety. Such a plan should include (a) a review of the threat or violent act, (b) escape and refuge, and (c) legal recourse.

A review of any incidents of abuse or threat of abuse allows the CSO to reflect on the importance of self-protection and the need to develop a plan for safety, especially if children are involved. CSOs need to understand from the start of counseling that the most important issue is their safety. If they believe their welfare or that of anyone in their care is in danger, they need to exit the situation immediately. You may discuss what CSOs need to exit (e.g., money and essentials) and how they will exit the situation. When they leave the situation, CSOs need to have a safe place to stay (e.g., in a domestic violence shelter or with friends or family) and need to consider their legal options. This is only an introduction to developing a safety plan; however, it does provide you with the essentials to work with CSOs who might report threats or actual violence. Furthermore, it is always wise to seek supervisory guidance when dealing with violent situations and SUD SOs.

The First Few Sessions

Once the initial contact has been made and the client and counselor agree to establish treatment, the counselor needs to focus on three domains: (a) educating the CSO about substance use disorders, (b) identifying the client's emotional and behavioral reactions, and (c) ensuring the CSO's self-care. Educating significant others about substance use disorders is an essential component of the treatment process. Education provides an introduction to substance use disorders in a nonjudgmental way and begins to answer many questions CSOs have about their loved one's behavior. It is important that the counselor feel comfortable providing basic information about substance use disorders, including symptoms of alcohol and other drug dependence, such as tolerance, withdrawal, and use despite consequences, and the effects of substance use and abuse on the brain. It is also helpful to provide some information on the clinical course of substance use disorders as well as relapse and recovery.

Most CSOs enter treatment with two overarching questions: Why does their loved one use drugs, and why can't he or she stop? After listening to the presenting problem and asking questions to clarify any issues, you might say, "I understand that your wife's drinking and drug use have affected you and that you wish she could stop right away. It is hard. Sometimes people can really turn it around once they decide to stop and accept help. Although people who abuse alcohol or other drugs have many reasons for their use or explanations for why they started using, actual addiction occurs in the brain. Because alcohol and other substance abuse affects the family as well, your family will need to participate in her recovery. It does take time and some work on everyone's part. But, more important, substance use disorders are treatable illnesses."

In this example, you point out to the CSO that change is possible but usually does not happen overnight and that everyone is expected to play a role in helping the loved one, as well as themselves, through this process. More important, the education helps to define substance use disorders and provides a frame from which the remainder of the clinical work proceeds.

CSOs often ask specific questions about use, recovery, and relapse. You simply need to remain empathic and nonjudgmental when providing information. Following are a few common questions and ways that you might respond using empathy and education:

1. A client might ask, "If he loves me, why can't he stop using drugs?" You might say, "It is hard to believe that someone who loves you would hurt you this way. However, your significant other's behavior is affected by his dependence on drugs."
2. If a client asks, "Why does she drink so much? How much can she take?" you might say, "It is scary to imagine. She has likely developed a tolerance for the amount that she is drinking and needs to drink that same amount or more to experience a high."
3. A client might ask, "Does alcohol cause a person to get depressed?" You could say, "It sounds like you have seen your significant other depressed and you wonder whether alcohol might be the cause. Alcohol is a depressant and may cause temporary sadness, tearfulness, and irritability."
4. If a client says, "He says that he wouldn't need to use coke if I didn't nag him so much. Is that true?" you might respond, "It is hard not to react emotionally to someone you see hurting himself when you feel so powerless to change it. Nagging alone does not cause someone to use alcohol or drugs, but within a certain context, relationship distress (like arguing) may lead to poor decision making and less impulse control by the user. If a drug is consumed, the user can then blame you."
5. A client might say, "People at work smoke pot all the time, and he associates with all of them. Should he socialize with them?" You could answer, "You are really concerned for him and are really thinking

about what might be responsible for his use. It is difficult to remain clean and sober when friends are using. His friends may be a trigger to use. A trigger is anything that reminds him of using and creates a desire to use. Sometimes this may happen outside of his awareness."

6. If a client asks, "Should there be alcohol in the house if he has a drinking problem?" you might say, "This is a very common issue. Having alcohol in the home provides easy access to it. It may also send a mixed message and run counter to your goal to help him to stop drinking."

7. If a client asks, "How can I help him stop?" you might say, "It is great that you want to help him. By initiating this treatment process, you have already begun to help."

These examples illustrate the various ways educational opportunities present themselves in the initial sessions with CSOs. Further educational work with CSOs continues throughout the therapeutic relationship.

Other educational opportunities exist outside the counseling sessions through participation in self-help support programs, such as Al-Anon and Alateen. These programs give adults and teens who are related to or friends with an alcoholic support from their peers who have been similarly affected by someone's alcoholism. The philosophy that guides these programs is adapted from AA and is based on its 12 steps and 12 traditions. Nar-Anon is a similar self-help program for family and friends who have been affected by someone's drug use. Although these groups may advocate different concepts from those discussed in this chapter, their usefulness to significant others is noteworthy. They meet in the community and are accessible both throughout the day and during the evening hours, when most counselors are not.

CRAFT

As CSOs become more engaged in the treatment process and a working alliance has been established, the counselor begins to address emotional and behavioral reactions between the SUD SO and the CSO. The CSO likely starts to disclose more details of his or her interactions with the SUD SO, and these descriptions provide clues to the CSO's overall distress and the SUD SO's substance-using behavior. To address this issue, counselors can use perspectives, techniques, and strategies from family systems and the CRAFT model (Smith & Meyers, 2004). The CRAFT model is a detailed approach to working with CSOs and draws on several strategies and techniques. The beginning counselor should also read Smith and Meyers's (2004) text and obtain supervision when implementing CRAFT techniques. Although a comprehensive discussion of the model extends beyond the scope of this chapter, a brief description of the model is given, and selected strategies are discussed.

A common perspective from the family systems tradition is the view that alcohol and other substances reshape the way family members interact with each other. For example, a wife may react differently to her husband when he is drunk than when he is sober. He may be quiet and boring when sober but sometimes playful and more enjoyable when he is drunk. The counselor may wonder what purpose alcohol serves in this situation and for whom. Do some of the ways the wife interacts with her husband encourage his drinking rather than his sobriety? Does he drink to replace something missing in himself and his marriage? These are important questions, and answers to them provide clues to the function of alcohol in the family or social group and how alcohol or other substance use may be unconsciously reinforced. These questions provide a bridge to the CRAFT model.

CRAFT is an empirically based model and provides a clear guide for working with CSOs (Meyers, Miller, Smith, & Tonigan, 2002; W. R. Miller, Meyers, & Tonigan, 1999). The model uses behavioral, nonconfrontational strategies to help CSOs reduce their emotional reactions to the SUD SO that may unintentionally facilitate further alcohol or substance misuse. In other words, the CSO discovers ways to reinforce abstinence and discourage substance use behavior without nagging, threatening, demanding, or otherwise promoting further use. These methods put the CSO in a better emotional position to positively support a decision by the SUD SO to accept treatment. Counselors using CRAFT have been able to help many CSOs increase their own overall satisfaction while successfully helping their loved ones accept treatment approximately 70% of the time (Smith & Meyers, 2004). Once CSOs agree to create interactions that promote abstinence and are willing to address their own behavior, the following CRAFT steps can be used.

In sessions, the counselor works with the CSO to identify patterns of interaction with the SUD SO that may reward positive steps toward abstinence. The counselor should listen for elements that suggest reinforcement of reductions in substance-using behavior. A reinforcer may be anything that influences a person to work toward receiving a reward for a particular behavior. For the CSO, a cessation of alcohol- or substance-abusing behavior is reinforcing. For example, if the SUD SO discontinues his or her use of alcohol or other drugs, the CSO feels some relief. A kiss and hug from the CSO as a reward for not using any substances is positively reinforcing to the SUD SO. The counselor should ask the CSO to identify practical reinforcements that positively encourage abstinence. For example, you might say, "What are some things both of you enjoy together that may serve to reinforce abstinence from drinking or using other substances?"

The CSO then makes a list of rewards (e.g., activities, events, gifts) that can be offered when the SUD SO is abstinent. The CSO also explicitly expresses to the SUD SO that the reward is being given for abstinence. The reward and the verbal reinforcement are critical to establishing the healthier interaction. You may need to role-play this interaction with the CSO until he or she feels comfortable. For example, a CSO states that her husband enjoys watching television with her when he comes home from work. When he has been drinking, however, neither of them watch television because they are arguing about his drinking. You might say, "Sounds like watching television together may be a positive reinforcer of abstinence. It is something to look forward to when he is not drinking. When he returns home from work and he has not been drinking, you can say to him that you are very happy that he is not drinking today and that because he is not drinking, you and he can relax together and watch television for the evening."

In this example, you identify a practical, doable, positive reinforcer that the SUD SO enjoys and that can be readily offered as an incentive for continued abstinence. If a CSO has difficulty creating a list, you only need to listen for already existing reinforcers or provide a general mix of enjoyable activities or gift items. Most CSOs will have little trouble developing a list.

Next, the counselor helps the CSO identify appropriate negative consequences for alcohol or other substance use behavior. You might say, "Now we need to consider healthy ways to discourage alcohol or other substance use. What are some things you can do to alert your wife that you are aware that she is using and that it is not acceptable?" If the CSO has difficulty identifying ways to alert the abuser in an appropriate, nonconfrontational manner, you might say, "Perhaps there are existing reinforcers that you can withhold. These might include giving kisses, watching television, or having dinner together."

The important issue is that the CSO withholds something that the SUD SO has come to appreciate and value and that without that reinforcer the SUD SO will feel a loss, perhaps enough to encourage abstinence. In addition, the CSO needs to explicitly express that the reinforcer (e.g., kisses) is being withheld because of the SUD SO's alcohol or substance use. These steps are essential to shifting the homeostatic pattern and to creating an environment that facilitates abstinence.

Putting It Together

This is a lot of material, so let's turn to a brief example that highlights the initial contact, the first session, and the key skills and techniques you need to begin work with CSOs.

A mother contacts a counselor and reports that her adult son abuses crack cocaine and marijuana on a regular basis; he has lost his job and lives with her. After further questioning to clarify some issues, the counselor learns that the mother supports her son financially. The counselor listens to her describe her situation and her feelings about her son's use of drugs. The following might be an exchange between the counselor and the mother:

Counselor: How has his use made you feel?
CSO: I feel terrible. Looking at him and seeing what he is doing to himself breaks my heart.

Counselor: It is hard to watch someone you care about hurt himself with drugs.

CSO: It is just so sad. I don't know what to do. It scares me, too.

Counselor: What scares you?

CSO: That I may get a call in the middle of the night that something terrible has happened to him. I don't think I can handle that.

Counselor: It is scary. Sounds like you have reached a point where it has become too hard to bear alone, and you recognized that you needed help. How long has this been going on?

CSO: He started using drugs when he was around 16 years old, and it has worsened over the last 2 years. He smokes pot every day, but I don't know how often he uses crack cocaine. I don't understand why he just can't stop. He cries sometimes when I talk to him about it, and he seems to go a few days without using, but then he goes right back to smoking pot.

Counselor: It is hard to understand why someone as young as he is would hurt himself by using drugs. For some people, using drugs becomes a daily activity, and they increase their use to achieve a high. This is called tolerance. It is not so easy to simply stop once addiction to a drug occurs. Although his use may be triggered by stress, peer pressure, or boredom, addiction occurs in the brain. So when he uses crack cocaine, he essentially changes the way his brain functions.

CSO: I was wondering why he uses. I thought it was because of me and how things went with his father and me.

Counselor: Parents often feel a sense of responsibility for their children's behavior and begin to search their history for explanations for their children's alcohol- or substance-abusing behavior. Well, you are not alone with that feeling, and many parents and families I have worked with have shared similar feelings. I have also seen many of these families rediscover their love and compassion for one another. It is not easy to stop using right away, but it gets easier, once he accepts help and both of you agree to work together to achieve sobriety.

CSO: That's what I want. I will do whatever it takes to help him stop smoking that stuff.

Counselor: You clearly want to help, and it takes a certain level of courage to step out of the situation and realize that help is needed. So, maybe we can take a closer look at what happens between the two of you—that will help me understand how you feel, and it may provide clues to his use.

CSO: Okay.

So far, the counselor has listened empathically, reflected back to the mother thoughts and feelings she has conveyed, and asked additional questions to better understand how she feels about her son's use and the toll it has had on her. The counselor has also provided some education about substance use disorders and offered the mother hope. Once a sufficient alliance was established with the mother and she showed willingness to participate in the recovery process, the counselor shifted the conversation to consider the interaction between the client and her son. This example is brief and only illustrates how a session or a few sessions might begin. Most sessions require more discussion of negative consequences (e.g., legal or medical issues) and feelings, because many CSOs have held on to their feelings for some time and finally have a chance to share them. So, in summary, you need to

1. listen empathically,
2. ask questions to deepen understanding,
3. provide education, and
4. shift to exploring the interactions between the CSO and the SUD SO when sufficient alliance has been established.

A final important factor you must remain aware of when working with CSOs is self-care. CSOs, in general, spend excessive time thinking about how to help the SUD SO stop using and less time thinking about their own lives. Their worry and concern for their loved one are tremendous and often interrupt their daily activities, at times to their own detriment. Some CSOs report feeling depressed (e.g., difficulty sleeping, excessive worry, tearfulness) and are in need of self-care. The counselor is in a position to raise the CSO's awareness of this critical issue and assist him or her in shifting some of the focus away from the SUD SO and onto himself or herself. For example, a counselor might say, "You are very involved with your son, trying to prevent him from using perhaps more than he is trying. In fact, you have missed work, have cried often, and have lost focus on other areas of your life that need your attention. Does this sound healthy to you?"

Most CSOs can see the obvious and will likely answer that this is not a healthy way to live their life. Even so, they do not know what else to do. The counselor might follow up by saying, "Your health is most important, and, given that your son will need you to make this change, it is equally important for you to focus on your own health and to increase happiness in other areas of your life. I bet there are things that you enjoy doing but have not done because of your worrying about your son. This is a good time to start enjoying them again. If there are things that you have avoided or tasks that you have allowed to pile up, then this is the time to reinvest that energy to completing them."

As the treatment progresses, the counselor may determine that family therapy would be a useful intervention. A family therapy approach may be effective when (a) the CSO has implemented some of the CRAFT strategies on a consistent basis; (b) the counselor suspects additional clinical attention is needed for other family members, such as children, parents, or siblings; and (c) the SUD SO has some record of abstinence and can at least agree on a plan of recovery for the family. When you refer a CSO and his or her family for family therapy, it is important to thoroughly discuss with the CSO your rationale for doing so. Explain that family therapy will allow for the examination of the entire family's patterns of interaction with the SUD SO and help determine good alternatives to interaction patterns that have not been helpful in the past. Additionally, family therapy improves communication between family members and provides immediate solutions to familial distress. It is important to remember that your client is the CSO, and therefore only the CSO can extend an invitation for family therapy.

If the CSO agrees to a referral for family therapy, then the counselor needs to offer the CSO contact information for a few family therapists in the local area. Family therapists are varied in their training and expertise. Some have a master's degree (e.g., master's in social work), whereas others have a doctoral degree in psychology (e.g., doctor of philosophy). Other family therapists have postgraduate training in marital and family therapy. Working with CSOs necessitates becoming familiar, for referral purposes, with family therapy practitioners in your local area.

Working with CSOs can be challenging and rewarding. This chapter contains a lot of material. Now it is your turn to put it all together.

Readings and Resources

Brown, S., & Lewis, V. (1999). *The alcoholic family in recovery.* New York: Guilford Press.

This book explores the challenges families face as they transition from active addiction to recovery. It was written for professionals but may be helpful for significant others who seek a better understanding of the impact of addiction on the family system.

Smith, J. E., & Meyers, R. J. (2004). *Motivating substance abusers to enter treatment: Working with family members.* New York: Guilford Press.

This book provides specific details that help counselors begin to assist significant others using the CRAFT approach.

Steinglass, P., Bennett, L. A., Wolin, S. J., & Reiss, D. (1987). *The alcoholic family.* New York: Basic Books.

This book presents significant research on the effects of alcoholism on the family system. Although it was written in 1987, it provides rich accounts of how alcoholism and families coexist to create a family environment that revolves around the alcoholic. Insights from the book remain relevant today.

Nar-Anon Family Groups World Service:
   http://nar-anon.org/index.html
Al-Anon and Alateen: www.al-anon.alateen.org/

Exercises

E.11.1. Empathy for a CSO

Demonstrate empathy for a CSO. Role-play in your team a scenario similar to those in this chapter. The significant other is contacting you for the first time and is in distress. Each team member will have a chance to role-play the empathic counselor. Note your feelings and other reactions as counselor, CSO, and observer. This will be part of your workbook log.

E.11.2. Role-Play: Educating CSO About Substance Use Disorders

Role-play a CSO who is worried about a loved one (child or partner) and who has many questions about substance use disorders. The counselor needs to provide empathy and education, and the observer keeps notes about the interaction. Practice explaining substance dependence and tolerance to the CSO. Each member of the role-play team will have a chance to experience each role. Pay attention to how each member feels in each role, and note it in your log.

E.11.3. Role-Play: Eliciting More Information From CSO

Consider the following scenario: A CSO reports that her mother drinks heavily on weekends and often fails to go to work on Mondays. The CSO often calls her mother's workplace to report that her mother is sick and unable to work. The CSO feels overwhelmed and is having difficulty sleeping. If you were her counselor, what else would you like to know? What additional questions would you ask? Role-play asking additional questions to deepen your understanding of the problem and the way the CSO and her mother interact with each other.

E.11.4. Role-Play Strategies

In the above scenario, how would you introduce the strategies from CRAFT? In your role-play teams, the counselor will assist the CSO in determining doable, practical reinforcers as well as discuss ways to discourage use by withholding certain reinforcers that the SUD SO values. Remember to instruct the CSO to explain to the user why he or she is providing or withholding the reinforcer.

E.11.5. Self-Care Discussion

In the above scenario, how would you discuss self-care with the CSO? What would you suggest?

Chapter 12

Considerations of Diversity in Substance Abuse Counseling

This chapter focuses on cultural factors that play a role in substance abuse treatment. It is important to recognize that most substance abuse treatments were created and validated with male, Caucasian clients and that there has been little research into the effectiveness of these treatments for other populations. In fact, there is some evidence that African Americans and Latino/a clients do not improve as much as White clients in substance abuse treatment (S. Sue & Lam, 2002). Thus, it is important to consider cultural factors when treating culturally diverse clients. A goal of this chapter is to discuss challenges in substance abuse treatment raised by cultural differences and provide guidance to help you overcome them.

Introduction, Definitions, and Basic Principles

First, a few important terms must be defined. *Multicultural counseling* means that the cultures of the counselor and client are different (Welfel, 2006). *Culturally diverse clients* are clients from any group that has suffered discrimination and oppression (Welfel, 2006). *Multicultural competency* refers to the knowledge, skills, and attitudes that counselors should have to help clients from cultural backgrounds other than their own. *Acculturation* refers to the degree to which immigrants and their families have adapted to the cultural values of the United States. Typically, each successive generation born in the United States becomes more integrated into American culture.

Cultural issues that are important to consider include the impact of stigmatization and oppression on minority groups, cultural differences that affect treatment considerations, and modifications to treatment as usual (TAU) that the counselor must make to take these factors into account. I discuss cultural considerations in regard to the key concepts addressed earlier in the book: empathy, the therapeutic relationship, and BSGS. I also discuss some important treatment considerations for special populations, including women; African Americans; Latino/as; Native Americans; Asians; clients who have a disability, are severely physically ill, or have an unusual appearance; gay, lesbian, bisexual, and transgendered clients; and recent immigrants.

Professional Ethics and Multicultural Counseling

Substance abuse counselors are ethically bound to treat all clients fairly and as effectively as they can. The Ethical Canon for substance abuse counselors, developed by NAADAC, the Association for Addiction Professionals (2008), states in Principle 1: Non-Discrimination,

> I shall affirm diversity among colleagues or clients regardless of age, gender, sexual orientation, ethnic/racial background, religious/spiritual beliefs, marital status, political beliefs, or mental/physical disability. I shall strive to treat all individuals with impartiality and objectivity relating to all based solely on their personal merits and mindful of the dignity of all human persons. As such, I shall not impose my personal values on my clients. I shall avoid bringing personal or professional issues into the counseling relationship. Through an awareness of the impact of stereotyping and discrimination, I shall guard the individual rights and personal dignity of my clients. I shall relate to all clients with empathy and understanding no matter what their diagnosis or personal history.

Multicultural Competence

The attitudes, knowledge, and skills a counselor needs to take into account cultural issues in counseling are best thought of as multicultural competence. Multicultural competence can be seen as having three broad dimensions:

1. being aware of one's own assumptions, values, and biases;
2. understanding the worldviews of culturally diverse clients; and
3. developing appropriate intervention strategies and techniques for diverse clients (D. W. Sue & Sue, 2008).

With regard to the first dimension of multicultural competence, counselors should become aware of their values, biases, and personal beliefs about human nature. Self-reflection, discussed earlier in the book, helps counselors develop an honest awareness of themselves and their beliefs. Although counselors are expected to provide counseling services to clients regardless of the clients' cultural background or other factors, such as lifestyle choice, they are human and are subject to misconceptions and prejudice regarding clients from backgrounds differing from their own. Thus, the first step in multicultural competence is a willingness to make an honest appraisal of one's personal views regarding cultural, lifestyle, religious, and ethnic differences one may encounter in counseling. When counselors find misconceptions and prejudice in themselves, their first obligation is to ensure that these prejudices do not cause harm to clients or compromise their treatment. A second obligation is to work to overcome these prejudices and misconceptions.

The second dimension of multicultural competence means that counselors make an effort to understand clients who have a cultural background different from their own. Counselors need to be alert to cultural practices that may be important to the client but that counselors are not familiar with. For example, if arranged marriage is an aspect of the client's cultural background, it is important to understand the practice without prejudging it. Counselors can, as a first step, ask clients to explain the practice so they can get a better understanding of it. If the issue is central to the client's recovery, it may be necessary to consult with a cultural representative, such as a rabbi or other spiritual leader. Clients' cultural backgrounds may advocate child-rearing practices, roles of women and wives, cultural dress codes, and dietary practices that are foreign to the counselor's own beliefs. It is the counselor's responsibility to try to understand these practices as they relate to helping the client. Counselors also must be attuned to potential prejudice and stigma that may affect culturally diverse clients. They must recognize and be sympathetic to the oppression that has affected minority clients.

The third dimension of cultural competence relates to developing skill in treating culturally diverse clients. In this regard, the focus in this chapter is on the effect of cultural factors on the therapeutic relationship, empathy, and BSGS.

The Therapeutic Relationship and Culture

In this book, the therapeutic relationship has been emphasized as an important element in the counseling process. Cultural factors may affect the counseling relationship in a number of ways. On the most obvious level, cultural differences may complicate the development of an open, trustful relationship with the client. Professional relationships in other cultures and groups may not correspond to the counselor's own understanding. Cultures vary in their acceptance of professional counseling help. Some cultures do not have a tradition of accepting help outside their cultural community; other cultural groups are not at all familiar with the professional role of the counselor. Thus, counselors may need to take extra time to explain the role they play, meet with the client's family and community members, and find culturally appropriate ways of explaining the role of the treatment to the client. Fuentes et al. (2006) conducted a study that highlights the importance of cultural competence to the therapeutic relationship. They found that clients who gave high ratings of cultural competence to their counselors also gave them high ratings on trustworthiness and empathy. Additionally, Burckell and Goldfried (2006) found that gay clients rated the quality of the therapeutic relationship as being as important as having a counselor who was gay-affirming and knowledgeable about gay issues.

Empathy and Culture

The nature and expression of empathy vary among cultural groups. Greetings, physical closeness, degree of formality, and expression of emotion all differ. For example, some cultural groups have more or less formal ways of relating to people outside of the family than is typical in American culture. If the client's culture supports a very formal relationship to nonfamily members, the counselor's typical demeanor may be experienced as intrusive. Thus, smiling when greeting a client, ordinarily seen as an open, friendly communication, might be perceived as unprofessional. Conversely, if the client's culture supports an informal and open relationship to nonfamily members, the counselor may be perceived as not concerned or involved with the client's problems if he or she takes a more professional demeanor. In this case, a professional manner may be interpreted as a lack of caring. In instances like this, it is a good idea to discuss the client's expectations and accommodate them as much as possible. An attitude of respect and efforts to help the client feel comfortable go a long way toward overcoming these potential barriers.

Language and Vocabulary Differences

American English is a highly nuanced language with unique metaphors that may not be fully understood by clients who are not native American English speakers. Counselors should be alert to using metaphors or sayings that nonnative American English speakers might not understand. For example, many expressions are based on American sports, such as baseball, football, and basketball (e.g., "slam dunk"), which immigrants may not be familiar with.

A greater challenge occurs when clients have a limited ability to speak and understand English. If the counselor does not speak the client's primary language, he or she cannot function as the primary counselor. Still, the counselor must remain respectful and communicate as effectively as possible. For example, if many clients in the clinic are fluent in another language, such as Spanish, the counselor should learn some key phrases in that language. The counselor working with a client who does not speak English well needs to be patient, find a colleague who speaks the client's primary language, and learn how to use hand gestures in a respectful manner. If the counselor makes a referral, he or she should write the information down clearly and neatly. The client's children or other family members may be able to read it. Using maps to show the referral location may also be helpful.

The client's cultural background may include beliefs about drinking and drug taking that affect the goals for treatment. For example, Islam views any use of alcohol negatively. Thus, controlled drinking would not be considered an acceptable goal for a client in a religious Muslim family and community. Some Native Americans may view taking hallucinogens as a spiritual activity and distinct from out-of-control use of drugs and alcohol. Thus, counselors must balance their concern about potential relapse to substance abuse with respect for the client's cultural beliefs.

Subtle prejudice and racism on the part of counselors may also affect treatment (Brinson, Brew, & Denby, 2008). Such prejudice is evident in ethnic jokes, which, for that reason, should never be used in counseling.

It is not easy to be objective about one's cultural competence. For example, one study showed that students in graduate counseling courses rated themselves as significantly more culturally competent than observers rated the students in a role-play involving multicultural competence (Cartwright, Daniels, & Zhang, 2008). On a more positive note, in another study, White students demonstrated higher levels of cultural competence after providing counseling services to non-White clients (Vereen, Hill, & McNeal, 2008).

Sometimes, despite our best intentions, we make errors. This can certainly occur with respect to cultural differences. A counselor may say something that, on reflection, is disrespectful to the client's ethnicity, culture, or lifestyle. For example, you may reflexively cringe when you see that a new client you thought was a woman is actually a man who is cross-dressed. You should reflect on whether you can be objective about discussing this topic with the client. If you think you can, it is important to genuinely discuss your reaction, indicating that you respect the client's choice to dress as a woman but that you have some old attitudes that you have not yet resolved. Alternatively, if you feel you cannot be objective, you should acknowledge that and offer the client a referral to a counselor who can.

Sometimes cultural differences may be "the elephant in the room" for both the counselor and the client. In such situations, it is wise and courageous to bring up the differences (D. W. Sue & Sue, 2008). For example, an African American counselor might say to a Euro-American client, "I wonder how you feel that I'm African American and you're White? Is it something that we should talk about and clear the air?"

What are reasonable accommodations to cultural differences? Perhaps the most important guideline is the counselor's genuineness. If the accommodation violates your own values and beliefs, it will be hard to be an effective counselor. For example, if the counselor is a feminist and the client's cultural background assumes a deferential role for women, it may be difficult for the counselor to be objective in balancing the client's cultural practices with his or her own belief in women's rights.

Inevitably, most counselors discover that there are some clients they cannot help, whether because of the client's culture, lifestyle, appearance, disability, or other characteristics. In these circumstances, a referral is appropriate. It is both respectful and accurate to make the referral by saying something like, "Unfortunately, I am unable to be of help to you because of my lack of knowledge and skill for your particular situation. For that reason, I believe it would be best to make a referral to a counselor who is." Although referral to a counselor of a background similar to the client's might be best, the counselor should explore this question with the client rather than make assumptions.

At times, clients' cultural beliefs may clash with safety, health, and legal concerns. For example, when a client brings up cultural discipline practices that approve of physical punishment, the counselor can elicit the client's views and mention the provisions of child abuse laws. He or she must also mention that counselors are legally required to report suspected cases of child abuse.

Incorporating Cultural Factors Into BSGS

Use of BSGS can help ensure that multicultural counseling concerns are properly addressed in sessions. With just some modest adjustments to the model, counselors can include multicultural issues in their session goals, techniques, and evaluations:

1. Does the goal of the session need to be modified because of cultural issues?
2. Given cultural considerations, do any of the techniques need to be modified?
3. Are the client, family, and community satisfied with the outcome?

For example, suppose your client is a Native American who is not fully acculturated into Western culture but does not fully identify with Native American culture. Suppose he will be discharged from the detoxification unit shortly and that you are responsible for the referral.

1. The goal is to make the proper referral. You need to determine whether the client should be referred to a substance abuse clinic, a Native American healer, a Native American treatment program, or a combination of options. This depends on what the client feels would be most helpful.
2. With regard to techniques, you can problem solve, reflect, summarize, and offer suggestions. Obviously, although you may not be knowledgeable about Native American cultural practices that promote recovery, you must be open-minded about them, support them,

and help the client move in that direction if that is what he wants to do. You may need to do some research to determine the available resources for the client.

3. To evaluate the outcome, follow up with the client to determine whether the cultural issues that arose have been addressed.

The following is an imagined dialogue for this situation:

Counselor: You will be leaving here in 2 days; have you thought about how you would like to continue your recovery?

Client: You know, I don't trust AA; it's Christian-based. I would have trouble feeling comfortable there. I've tried it.

Counselor: What else is out there?

Client: Are there any treatment programs that are not AA-based? Like this cognitive–behavioral thing?

Counselor: Yes. There is a pretty good program called Matrix. These programs use the treatment approaches with the most research support. Although they recommend AA and NA, they focus on many other ways you can recover. [For more information about Matrix, see the Readings and Resources section at the end of the chapter.] Let's see if there's a location you can reach. . . . I know you have worked to connect to your Native American culture. Do you think it would be a good idea to continue that?

Client: You mean the medicine man stuff and the sweat lodges, the spiritual ways . . .

Counselor: Well, I'm no expert on your culture, but sometimes people gain from feeling connected to their roots and can find an identity and strength from their culture. After all, it's important to have meaning in life, and that may help you stay away from alcohol as much as anything else. What do you think?

Client: I'm surprised that you could say that. I thought you just saw me as a client who needed substance abuse treatment. But I think, yes, if I can feel like a real Pueblo tribal member and really become a good example for the young kids, I would feel much better about myself.

Counselor: So, what would be a good first step in that direction?

Client: There are two elders I would like to talk to.

Counselor: Do you have their telephone numbers? Would you like to call them from here?

Client: Okay.

The cultural accommodations in this imagined dialogue include understanding the client's objections to AA and NA, bringing up cultural issues, and encouraging the client to contact the tribal elders. The *DSM–IV–TR* provides an outline for cultural formulation that is similar to the BSGS approach presented here (American Psychiatric Association, 2000, pp. 897–898).

Specific Populations

Generalizations about any ethnic, cultural, or minority group must be balanced with the understanding that a specific client may or may not conform to these generalizations. Thus, although they are often true, the following generalizations must be verified before one can assume the client reflects the generalization (D. W. Sue & Sue, 2008).

Women With Substance Use Disorders

Women are far outnumbered by men in most substance abuse treatment programs. Therefore, counselors must be sensitive to the needs of women and make sure they are respected by both clients and staff. These difficulties can be overcome by the use of women's groups or multifamily counseling in conventional programs and by separate women's treatment programs. Multifamily counseling may enhance women's outcome in conventional programs, because their families show support for their recovery (Boylin, Doucette, & Jean, 1997). Specially designed long-term residential programs for pregnant or parenting women with substance use disorders have a success rate of 68% to 71% when women remain in treatment at least 6 months (Greenfield et al., 2004).

One aspect of treating women is making sure to provide help and expertise where it is needed. In addition to the substance use disorder, counselors should evaluate pregnancy, sexually transmitted disease, partner violence, parenting issues, and history of trauma (National Association of State Alcohol and Drug Abuse Directors, 2008). Women with substance use disorders often have a history of trauma and suffer from PTSD (Center for Substance Abuse Treatment, 2005c). Treatment of co-occurring PTSD and substance use disorders requires significant modification from TAU (see Chapter 10). Lesbian women may be more likely to have co-occurring disorders than heterosexual women (Ross & Durkin, 2005).

Additionally, women must overcome more barriers to treatment than men: They often have multiple demands on their time, including parenting responsibilities, prenatal care, household responsibilities, and, particularly in the case of single mothers, full-time employment. Thus, counselors need to help women solve these practical problems to overcome barriers to treatment. In addition, feminist therapy (S. Sue & Lam, 2002) may be a useful intervention for some women. Even if the treatment is not feminist oriented, feminist views should be respected and encouraged.

African American Clients With Substance Use Disorders

D. W. Sue and Sue (2008) made several suggestions about multicultural counseling with African Americans. In particular, they suggested establishing an egalitarian relationship. In contrast to other ethnic groups, most African Americans tend to find a personal commonality with the counselor. This may be facilitated by counselor self-disclosure. If the client seems hostile or aloof, discussing some noncounseling topics may be useful. Determine whether and how the client has responded to discrimination and racism, in both healthy and unhealthy ways, and examine issues pertaining to racial identity. African Americans often prefer problem-solving and time-limited counseling approaches (D. W. Sue & Sue, 2008).

D. W. Sue and Sue (2008) suggested that, during the first session, it may be beneficial to bring up the client's reaction to having a counselor of a different ethnic background. The counselor could say, for example, "Sometimes clients feel uncomfortable working with a counselor of a different race. Would this be a problem for you?"

Latino/a Clients With Substance Use Disorders

Latino/as comprise a wide range of cultural diversity in themselves, coming from many countries in North America, Central America, and South America. The following customs seem to reflect most Latino/as' cultural background. D. W. Sue and Sue (2008) noted that less-acculturated Hispanic Americans expect a more formal professional interaction than is common in the United States. They may see substance abuse counselors as authority figures and expect them to be formally dressed. Conversely, as the counseling relationship develops, Hispanic clients may develop a close personal bond with the counselor. They may perceive the counselor as a family member or friend, invite him or her to family functions, and give him or her gifts.

If a client does not communicate well in English, it is better to refer him or her to a Spanish-speaking counselor. In reviewing confidentiality provisions, be sure to explain that immigration status will not be shared with immigration officials, should that be an issue.

In terms of the kind of treatment, Hispanics tend to prefer time-limited, solution-based therapies, and family therapy should be considered, because the family is very important in Hispanic culture (D. W. Sue & Sue, 2008). Should parenting issues arise in the treatment, keep in mind that physical discipline is used more often in Hispanic families than is common in the United States. Although women in general are stigmatized by substance use disorders, Latina women who have substance use disorders may be especially stigmatized in the Hispanic community.

Native American Clients With Substance Use Disorders

Native Americans have high rates of substance use disorders. Malcolm, Hesselbrock, and Segal (2006) noted that Native Americans have twice the expected rate of alcoholism; are seven times more likely to die of alcoholism than the average American; and are twice as likely to be hospitalized for alcoholism, substance abuse, or mental health problems. In a survey of Native American Alaskans in treatment for alcoholism, Malcolm et al. found that more than 50% were addicted to at least one additional drug.

French (2004) noted that Native Americans have a high rate of fetal alcohol syndrome.

Because of the long history of oppression, exploitation, and betrayal by the Euro-American population and agencies, it is essential for substance abuse counselors to be sensitive to multicultural issues for Native American clients. Euro-American colonization of Native American land led to the virtual destruction of the Native American culture and way of life (C. L. Johnson, 2006). War and disease have reduced the Native American population to 10% of what it was when Euro-Americans arrived (D. W. Sue & Sue, 2008). The violation of treaties and betrayals by many governmental agencies have led the Native American community to mistrust American institutions. Among the many destructive practices, it was once common to send Native American children to American-run boarding schools, where they were deprived of their native language and customs and contact with their community.

Many authors have referred to the multigenerational trauma cycle suffered by Native Americans (Gone, 2006; C. L. Johnson, 2006). That is, Native Americans have experienced continued betrayal and exploitation by the larger American institutions and culture throughout the history of interaction. Additionally, the traumas suffered by Native American parents have made them vulnerable to substance use and mental disorders and have often rendered them unable to effectively parent their children; thus, their children are put at risk for direct trauma.

As a result of these historical events, the possibility of true Native American identity has been shattered (Gone, 2006). Sixty percent of Native Americans are of mixed ethnic origin (D. W. Sue & Sue, 2008). Nonetheless, Native Americans may identify with or wish to become more identified with their cultural heritage. For this reason, Native American clients should be asked about their wishes in this regard. If they already are firmly identified with Native American culture, they may benefit from the traditional healing practices discussed below. If they wish to become more identified with their Native American background or are confused about what they want, it makes sense to contact Native American elders or healers for consultation and referral.

Substance abuse treatment for Native Americans can be divided into three options: traditional Native American treatment, blended treatment, and multicultural treatment. In many Native American communities, elders or healers may be able to use traditional approaches to help Native Americans overcome their substance use disorders (C. L. Johnson, 2006). These approaches are more spiritual in nature than the Western model of medicine. For example, the medicine wheel is a Native American concept that relates to helping individuals, families, and communities restore balance when problems such as substance use have affected people in the community. Some Native American communities have sweat lodges, places for ritual cleansing ceremonies that can be used to help people overcome substance use disorders. Clients can also tell the story of their recovery and request community support (BigFoot & Dunlap, 2006). Storytelling is an important aspect of Native American cultural healing and is often used to help clients understand and overcome their substance use disorder (BigFoot & Dunlap, 2006).

Blended treatment combines elements of Western beliefs with Native American culture. French (2004) referred to the formation of modified AA groups to incorporate the values, rituals, and worldview of Native American culture. He also discussed the Native American church, which consists of a blend of Christian and Native American beliefs. Key tenets of the church are abstinence from alcohol and other drugs but ritual use of peyote. The church was banned for a long period of time because of its use of peyote.

Venner, Feldstein, and Tafoya (2007) have set up a collaboration between MI behavioral health care workers and Native American communities to develop an MI treatment manual adapted for use with Native Americans with substance use disorders. They believe this is a promising approach, because MI has been shown to be the most effective conventional treatment for Native Americans with alcohol use disorders (Villanueva, Tonnigan, & Miller, 2007).

Native Americans may also choose to attend standard substance abuse treatment. Typically, these counseling settings are multicultural, because Native American counselors are fairly rare. The following considerations are important in multicultural treatment:

- Introduce yourself more fully, providing more personal information than usual about your background (Venner et al., 2007).
- Keep in mind that Native American and Western values are quite different and that you must respect your client's values. For example, sharing and cooperation are valued over competition in the Native American culture. Native Americans avoid eye contact as a sign of respect. In addition, the culture does not value material success to the same degree as the dominant Western culture (C. L. Johnson, 2006).
- Do not ask for details about spiritual practices, as many are private and sacred.
- Try not to hurry the client. Allow him or her time to finish statements and thoughts (D. W. Sue & Sue, 2008).
- Be sensitive to any Native American identity issues the client may have (see the above discussion on Native American identity).
- Seek consultation with and referral to Native American elders and healers when cultural issues emerge (Venner et al., 2007).

Asian American Clients With Substance Use Disorders

Although Asian Americans have a low prevalence rate of substance use disorders (Lee, Law, & Eo, 2003) and low rates of admission to substance abuse and mental health services (Chow, 2002), the Asian American community is rapidly growing in America (Lee et al., 2003; D. W. Sue & Sue, 2008), and more Asian Americans will likely require treatment for substance use disorders. Additionally, cultural factors may account for Asian Americans' underuse of mental health and substance abuse services. Asian Americans typically feel shame about having personal problems, are reluctant to turn to family for help, and fear losing face. They lack knowledge about psychotherapy and mental health services, and first-generation immigrants may not be fluent in English (Lee et al., 2003). For these reasons, a section on Asian Americans with substance use disorders is included in this chapter.

In general, Asian Americans embrace values that are somewhat different from those of typical Americans. This does, of course, vary depending on the degree of acculturation. Asian Americans often have a collectivistic orientation and emphasize family harmony and adherence to correct values (D. W. Sue & Sue, 2008). Asian American parents are typically more authoritarian than their American counterparts. They may show little interest in the child's viewpoint regarding family matters. Communication flows down from the parent to the child, who is expected to defer to the parent. Parents use emotional and physical punishment more than in the typical American family, and they may use shame and guilt to control their children. Children are expected to strive for family goals. Often in Asian American communities, expression of emotion is discouraged.

The following considerations are important in the treatment of Asian Americans with substance use disorders.

- Psychotherapy is a foreign concept to Asian Americans. Extra time should be spent carefully explaining the rationale for treatment (D. W. Sue & Sue, 2008).
- Use coconstruction: You and the client should work together to define the problem and develop solutions. The counselor is the expert on substance use disorders, but the client is the expert regarding his or her life (D. W. Sue & Sue, 2008).
- Asian American clients expect treatment to be time limited and to have concrete goals and strategies focused on solutions. CBT and solution-focused strategies are often well received. Goals may need to be modified to fit Asian American values. Assertiveness training may be appropriate for workplace situations but not in family contexts (D. W. Sue & Sue, 2008).
- A focus on emotions is not recommended for Asian American clients. Counselors should focus on behavior and problem solving rather than on emotions (D. W. Sue & Sue, 2008).
- Parent–child conflicts should be framed as acculturation conflicts (D. W. Sue & Sue, 2008).
- Ethnic-specific services for Asian Americans may be preferable for clients who have recently immigrated, identify closely with the Asian community, or have little command of English (Chow, 2002).

- Asian Americans may turn to family or herbal doctors for treatment of mental and substance abuse disorders (Lee et al., 2003). Counselors should collaborate with these Asian American healers when their clients use them.

Clients With Disabilities, Unusual Physical Appearance, or Severe Illness and Substance Use Disorders

When a client has a physical illness or a disability, it is appropriate to discuss the client's compliance with medical treatment, including whether he or she is taking medications. It is also appropriate to discuss any practical matters regarding the illness that you can help problem solve, such as disagreements the client may have with his or her physician, problems obtaining medication, or questions about which medical treatment to pursue.

Clients with substance use disorders have a higher rate of HIV infection than the general population. Counselors may have a fear of infection when treating HIV-infected clients (or clients with other illnesses). To deal with this fear, it is important to know how HIV is transmitted. Most agencies provide in-service education on this topic. It is extremely unlikely for HIV to be transmitted in the course of substance abuse counseling. Counselors may also find that homophobia affects their work counseling HIV-infected clients (homophobia is discussed later in the chapter).

In treating HIV-infected clients, keep in mind the following treatment considerations:

- Methadone maintenance is the preferred treatment for HIV-positive opiate-dependent women (Center for Substance Abuse Treatment, 2005a).
- Some HIV infection medication interacts with methadone (Center for Substance Abuse Treatment, 2005a). Thus, patients' complaints about the dosing of methadone should be taken seriously.
- Harm-reduction goals are appropriate (Center for Substance Abuse Treatments, 2000b, p. 159).
- HIV risk-reduction counseling (Center for Substance Abuse Treatment, 2000b, p. 93) is appropriate for most clients with substance use disorders as well as for HIV-infected clients. This counseling includes not only discussing safer practices to reduce the risk of being infected or infecting others but building motivation to do so. MI approaches can be used for the latter concern. You can ask all clients to fill out a risk assessment checklist (see Center for Substance Abuse Treatment, 2000b, p. 92).

Some clients may have disabilities, such as loss of motor function, vision loss, or hearing loss. It is essential that counselors be patient with these clients, extend the extra time that is necessary, and adapt their normal manner to provide a comfortable and safe environment. The suggestions made by D. W. Sue and Sue (2008) are sensible; if you reflect on them, you can intuit what clients may need by putting yourself in their shoes (i.e., empathy). For example, Sue and Sue recommended the following:

- For clients with physical disabilities, do not use or move items such as wheelchairs, crutches, or canes without permission; ask whether assistance is required before providing it; and sit at the client's eye level to facilitate comfort in communication.
- For clients with vision loss, offer the use of your arm and guide them. Let them know if you are moving about or if the conversation is to end. Give verbal cues when offering a seat, and place the client's hand on the back of the chair.
- For clients who are deaf or hard of hearing, realize that talking very loud does not enhance communication. To get the client's attention, call him or her by name. If the client does not respond, lightly touch him or her on the arm or shoulder. Do not pretend to understand if you do not. Make direct eye contact, and keep your face and mouth visible. Realize that communication may take longer than usual, and plan accordingly; do not rush. Also, remember that speech impediments do not indicate limited intelligence.
- For all clients with a disability, understand the prejudice, discrimination, inconveniences, and barriers they face. If the client's disability is related to his or her substance use disorder, determine whether the client blames himself or herself for the problem. Examine your own attitudes about people who incur a disability as the result of substance use. Engage the support of family members, and help them reframe the problem so that positives can be identified.

Other clients may have physical features that are stigmatized, such as obesity, dwarfism, or facial scars. First you must deal with your own personal reaction to these characteristics. Then you must learn to bring them into the dialogue in a neutral and accepting manner, because these features may be a factor tied to the client's substance use.

Gay, Lesbian, Bisexual, and Transgendered (GLBT) Clients With Substance Use Disorders

People who are not heterosexual, including GLBT people, have been discriminated against and oppressed for centuries. Although progress has been made in confronting these problems, there remains a great deal of oppression, stigma, and prejudice. When GLBT clients seek substance abuse treatment, their sexual orientation must be respected and supported. The effects of discrimination and oppression have had negative consequences for many GLBT clients. The counselor's first responsibility is to be sure that he or she does not continue or condone any such treatment.

This means using appropriate language to describe the GLBT culture and avoiding all derogatory terms about the culture. It means that the counselor should support gay rights and GLBT lifestyle choices as long as they are part of a good recovery plan. The counselor should also protect the confidentiality of clients' sexual orientation (Cheng, 2003).

Transgendered people are a diverse group of people who cross or transcend culturally defined categories of gender. They may cross-dress, and they may seek to change their physical characteristics through hormone therapy or sex reassignment surgery (Center for Substance Abuse Treatment, 2000b, p. 144). Counselors should address transgendered people with pronouns based on their self-identity (e.g., a man who self-identifies as female should be addressed with feminine pronouns). It is also appropriate to allow transgendered clients to use the restroom designated for their gender self-identity (Center for Substance Abuse Treatment, 2000b, p. 146).

Homophobia is often an important factor in the issues GLBT clients bring to treatment (Cheng, 2003). *Homophobia* refers to a person's conscious or unconscious fears about GLBT people. In heterosexual men, it may reflect fears about being gay and may be manifested in ugly incidents of assault such as are periodically noted in the news media. Most, if not all, gay men have had painful experiences at the hands of some homophobic heterosexual men. Lesbian women also have likely experienced prejudice and discrimination from homophobic men and women. Thus, the heterosexual counselor's first responsibility is to examine his or her feelings about GLBT people and determine whether he or she has some degree of homophobia so that he or she does not contribute further to oppression of this group. (See Figure 12.1 for a self-administered homophobia questionnaire.)

Although it may seem counterintuitive, GLBT people can also exhibit homophobia. Because of oppression from others, many GLBT people internalize homophobia, that is, they become ashamed of their GLBT identity. They may hide it from their parents, from their heterosexual friends, and at their place of work. Because of homophobia, oppression, and prejudice, GLBT people are subject to more stress in their daily life than many other groups. They may find relief in drugs and alcohol to escape these pressures, relieve their homophobia about being GLBT, and release any conflicts they may have about homosexual sex. For these reasons, GLBT people may develop a substance use disorder (Cheng, 2003).

After GLBT clients become abstinent, they may need to explore their homophobia, their experiences of oppression and prejudice, and any conflicts they may have about sex. GLBT clients should be encouraged to develop a GLBT sexual identity and to explore their lifestyle choices. There are two major pathways in society currently available for GLBT people. The openly GLBT lifestyle, with its own neighborhoods, entertainment, and other social opportunities is, fortunately, an option available in many communities today. GLBT clients' other choice is to live a more conven-

Figure 12.1

Homophobia Questionnaire for Counselors and Clients

Did you ever stop yourself from doing or saying certain things because someone might think you are gay or lesbian? What kind of things?

Do you ever intentionally do or say things so that people will not think you are gay or lesbian? What kind of things?

Do you think that lesbians or gays can influence others to become homosexual?

Do you think someone could influence you to change your sexual orientation?

If you are a parent, how would you (or do you) feel about having a lesbian daughter or gay son?

How do you think you would feel if you discovered that one of your parents, a parent figure, or a brother or sister were gay or lesbian?

Are there any jobs, positions, or professions that you think gays and lesbians should be barred from holding or entering? Which ones, and why?

Would you go to a physician whom you knew or believed to be gay or lesbian if he or she were a different gender from you? If he or she were the same gender as you? If not, why not?

If someone you cared about said to you, "I think I'm lesbian or gay," would you suggest that the person see a therapist?

Have you ever been to a gay or lesbian social club, party, bar, or sporting event? If not, why not?

Would you wear a button that says, "How dare you assume that I'm heterosexual?" If not, why not?

Can you think of three positive aspects of a lesbian or gay lifestyle? Can you think of three negative aspects of a heterosexual lifestyle?

Have you ever laughed at or told a "queer" joke?

Note. From *Substance Abuse Treatment for Persons With HIV/AIDS* (Technical Assistance Publication Series 37, DHHS Publication No. SMA 08-4137), by the Center for Substance Abuse Treatment, 2000, Figure 7-2, p. 134, Rockville, MD: Substance Abuse and Mental Health Services Administration.

tional lifestyle, perhaps cohabiting with a significant other but otherwise living much the same as their heterosexual neighbors. Although the latter option may reflect some lingering homophobia, if clients wish to pursue that path, their choice should be respected. In any event, counselors should be GLBT-affirming in their attitude and behavior (Burckell & Goldfried, 2006; Weber, 2008)

Some clients may feel more comfortable with a GLBT counselor or a GLBT-oriented substance abuse treatment program. Such choices should be respected (Cheng, 2003). GLBT clients should also be made aware of any self-help meetings specifically for gays that are available.

Substance abuse counselors (and other mental health professionals) should not initiate a discussion about changing a GLBT client's sexual orientation (Cheng, 2003). If clients are conflicted about their sexual identity and raise the issue, it can be explored. It is rare, however, for gay and lesbian clients to successfully change their sexual identity. More likely, the client can begin to see his or her internalized homophobia and accept his or her GLBT identity. As with other areas of clinical concern, the client's sexual issues may be deep rooted and may require more exploration and therapeutic work than a substance abuse counselor can handle. In that case, a referral to another mental health professional with expertise in this area is appropriate.

Recent Immigrants With Substance Use Disorders

Obviously, recent immigrants often lack basic information about American customs, regulations, and laws, so counselors must provide the information or advise the client about where to obtain it. Whether their immigration status is legal or not, recent immigrants may be concerned about the possibility of being deported. Immigration laws and their enforcement vary depending on region and current trends. Substance abuse counselors should be knowledgeable about any laws that may affect their clients. Reports provided to law enforcement should be carefully crafted to include only the required information.

In addition to adjusting to the United States, immigrant families are faced with different levels of acculturation within the extended family. A good deal of conflict can occur between parents who adhere to the country of origin's cultural values and their children, who often quickly adopt American values. The family's grandfather may basically still be keeping all of the customs of his country of origin, the parents may be somewhat acculturated, and the children may be completely acculturated. Of course, there are many other possibilities. The family may view teen drinking and drug taking through the lens of the original culture, which may be more or less permissive than the United States. Traumas suffered in the country of origin, mourning, refugee status, and culture shock may need to be explored. The meaning of psychiatric illness in that culture also may need to be examined, and if such illness is stigmatized, it may have to be normalized.

Readings and Resources

Sue, D. W., & Sue, D. (2008). *Counseling the culturally diverse* (5th ed.). Hoboken, NJ: Wiley.

This is a large, thoughtful, and often-referenced text.

The National Center for Cultural Competence has a Web site with information about cultural issues in counseling: www11.georgetown.edu/ research/gucchd/nccc/.

Information about the Matrix Institute's outpatient treatment programs can be found at www.matrixinstitute.org/Matrix%20Treatment%20 Program.htm.

Exercises

E.12.1. Client Characteristics

We all have personal dislikes. Name those characteristics, such as physical appearance, age, effeminacy (in men) or masculinity (in women), and obesity, that "turn you off." How would you handle it if you looked in the waiting room and saw that your new client had some of these characteristics?

E.12.2. African American Clients

How would you react if your African American client stated that when he was browsing through CDs in a record store, he felt that an employee was watching him closely as if the client might shoplift? (This scenario comes from Brinson et al., 2008.)

E.12.3. Non-English Speakers

Suppose a client did not speak English well. What goals would you have for the interaction? What techniques would you use? One person can role-play the client, and another can role-play the counselor.

E.12.4. People With Disabilities

Examine your attitudes toward people with disabilities. Do you feel differently about people who incurred their disability as a result of their substance use? How would this affect your counseling role?

E.12.5. Multicultural Role-Play

Using BSGS, choose a multicultural counseling situation to role-play. Be sure to include a discussion of cultural factors in Parts 1, 3, and 4.

Chapter 13

Treatment Plans and Clinical Writing

In this chapter, I discuss clinical writing. Substance abuse counselors must write many kinds of reports. The major kinds of reports are discussed in this chapter, including psychosocial narratives, admission and discharge summaries, treatment plans, and progress notes.

Ask any substance abuse counselor, and he or she will tell you that paperwork takes up a large percentage of time on the job. Thus, to survive as a counselor, you should have a good idea of how to perform the basic writing that will be required. Clinical writing is different from both academic and casual writing. Its purpose is to communicate the important clinical issues of the client and to document the therapeutic services provided to him or her. Clinical writing should be clear, concise, specific, and non-judgmental (Cameron & Turtle-Song, 2002). The most common categories of clinical writing are progress notes, psychosocial evaluations, and treatment plans, all of which are kept in individual files for each client, often called medical records or charts. In most clinics, a number of agencies will review these clinical records, including state licensing agencies, insurance companies, and accreditation agencies. Poor medical records can lead to severe penalties for the clinic, such as loss of significant revenue and even closure of the program.

I have created the imagined case of David Stone to illustrate clinical writing examples for this chapter. In this hypothetical case study, Mr. Stone was admitted to Recovery Center, where he was detoxified from alcohol. After 5 days, he was transferred to the rehabilitation unit, where he received group and individual counseling. The psychosocial narrative (Exhibit 13.2) and initial treatment plan (Exhibit 13.3) were created in this context. Nearing the end of Mr. Stone's 28-day stay at the rehabilitation unit, his counselor wrote a discharge summary and aftercare plan (Exhibit 13.4). Mr. Stone was then admitted to the Recovery Center's outpatient unit. The intake counselor at the outpatient clinic wrote an intake summary (Exhibit 13.5), and the primary counselor created a revised treatment plan for Mr. Stone's treatment at the outpatient clinic (Exhibit 13.6). The progress note (Exhibit 13.7) was written while Mr. Stone was in the outpatient clinic.

Psychosocial Evaluations and Psychosocial Narratives

The purpose of the psychosocial evaluation is to provide a relatively complete picture of the client as he or she enters treatment so that staff can determine whether admission is appropriate and, if so, what the appropriate treatment services are. The information is obtained in interviews with the client, during which the client usually fills out a number of forms or the counselor asks a large number of detailed questions. This information is then organized into a coherent document called the psychosocial narrative. Typically, a summary of the evaluation is read at the clinical case conference, where clinical staff meet to determine whether the client should be admitted to the facility, what services should be provided, and which clinical staff should provide the services. An outline for the psychosocial narrative is provided in Exhibit 13.1.

Two terms from Exhibit 13.1 need to be explained: *mental status* and *presenting problem*. *Mental status* refers to the current cognitive functioning and emotional state of the client. Psychiatrists do a full mental status examination of clients on the first visit. For the purposes of the psychosocial narrative, the counselor only needs to determine whether the client needs a psychiatric evaluation and a complete mental status examination. The questions in the "brief assessment of current mental status" section of Exhibit 13.1 should provide you with enough information to make that decision.

Presenting problem has a specific meaning in the mental health field; it refers to the reasons that brought the client to treatment. The presenting problem may differ from what the counselor considers the primary problem. For example, a client mandated to treatment might have come because his or her job is on the line. The counselor may be certain that the client has substance dependence, but the presenting problem is that the client's job is at risk. The counselor can use the presenting problem to build motivation, because it is what motivated the client to come for treatment.

Most agencies have a somewhat different format for the psychosocial narrative; you can adapt the outline given here to fit your agency's format. See Exhibit 13.2 for an example of a psychosocial narrative. The main consideration to keep in mind when writing the narrative is to provide the relevant information for the clinical staff to make admission and treatment

---

Exhibit 13.1

Outline for a Typical Psychosocial Narrative

First sentence: State the client's name, sex, age, marital status, appearance, and degree of cooperativeness or lack thereof.

Presenting problem: State the reason the client came for the interview.

Current pattern of use of substances:

- substances used,
- amounts,
- frequency, and
- effects.

Effects of substance use:

- physical dependence (acquired tolerance or withdrawal),
- psychological dependence,
- medical consequences,
- work impairments,
- family disruption,
- legal problems, and
- financial problems.

History of drug and alcohol use:

- first use;
- increases in amounts or frequency, circumstances of increases, and consequences of increases;
- efforts to stop alcohol or drug consumption and longest period of abstinence; and
- previous substance abuse treatment and outcome.

Client's education, work, and criminal justice history: Provide a brief summary of each area.

Current family information:

- description of current family unit,
- substance use and abuse in the family,
- support for recovery, and
- relevant atypical features of the family (e.g., severe mental illness, homelessness, trauma).

Family history:

- Describe siblings.
- Describe childhood.

(Continued)

> **Exhibit 13.1** *(Continued)*
> **Outline for a Typical Psychosocial Narrative**
>
> *Family history (Continued):*
>
> - Note any unusual features, such as childhood sexual abuse.
> - Note the client's childhood relationships to parents, siblings, and peers.
>
> *Brief assessment of current mental status:*
>
> - Does the client seem to have any moderate or severe mental illness?
> - Does he or she exhibit depression, anxiety, paranoia, or suicidal ideation?
> - Is the client intoxicated or otherwise impaired?
> - Are the client's speech, manner, and way of relating normal or odd? If odd, explain.
>
> *Clinical impressions:* Provide your best judgment about the following:
>
> - *Diagnostic impression:* Does the client show substance abuse or dependence? Indicate whether the client should have a psychiatric evaluation.
> - *Current status:* Indicate the client's current mood and attitude and the overall impression he or she gave in the session.
> - *Stage of change*
> - *Client's reaction to interview*
> - *Treatment recommendations*
>
> Date: _____
>
> _____
> *Signature of interviewer and credential earned*

decisions. Information for the initial treatment plan comes from this document. Information that may be interesting but not relevant to these tasks should be edited out. Brief relevant quotes made by the client, however, help the clinical staff get a clearer picture of the client. Any changes on the part of the client in the course of the session should be noted, as they provide clues to his or her ability to develop a therapeutic relationship (Cameron & Turtle-Song, 2002). In this hypothetical example, Mr. Stone warms up during the course of the interview; this is a positive sign.

Note that statements in the narrative are made with varying degrees of certainty. For example, the narrative states that the client is in precontem-

Exhibit 13.2
Example of a Psychosocial Narrative

David Stone is a single, 45-year-old unemployed African American man residing at the city shelter on 33rd Street. He was referred by his social worker because of a long history of drinking problems. After medical detoxification, Mr. Stone was admitted to the rehabilitation unit. He was somewhat guarded at the beginning of the interview, but by the end he was fully cooperative. Mr. Stone is a tall, thin man, slightly stooped and causally dressed in worn and somewhat disheveled clothing. His grooming was satisfactory, given that he is living in a shelter.

Mr. Stone stated he had come to counseling because it was a condition of his continued stay in the shelter, although he acknowledged that he had a drinking problem. He has had several detoxifications and treatment episodes, with little success. He stated that he had trouble accepting the religious aspect of AA, which made it difficult for him to fully get involved with the treatment programs.

When asked why he thought he had a drinking problem, Mr. Stone said that he had been drinking heavily since he was in the Army, as much as a fifth of vodka per day. He said that he originally drank to overcome shyness, and it quickly became an essential feature of his daily life. He stated that he has been arrested many times for fighting while intoxicated and lost several girlfriends because of violent behavior when drinking. His longest period of abstinence was for 2 months while he was in treatment at the Haven Alcoholism Clinic. He is fairly hopeless about ever being able to control or stop his drinking, although he expressed a willingness to "give it another try."

Mr. Stone grew up in Brooklyn with five brothers and sisters. He was the middle child. His mother was alcoholic, and his father abandoned the family when Mr. Stone was 6. He stated that life was difficult when he was a child, but his mother loved them all. They were often forced to move because of difficulty paying the rent. Mr. Stone did poorly in school; he stated that he just wasn't interested. He enlisted in the Army to get away from the unpleasantness of his home life. He adjusted well to the Army, except when his drinking took over, which caused his involvement in several fights. He was given a conditional discharge. Since that time, he has been engaged in manual labor employment for sporadic periods of time and on welfare.

He has had several girlfriends, including one woman with whom he has a son. He has not seen his son for 15 years. He recalls the relationship with the mother of his son fondly. It ended because of his drinking. His mother died several years ago, and he has sporadic contact with his brothers and sisters.

(Continued)

Exhibit 13.2 *(Continued)*
Example of a Psychosocial Narrative

Mr. Stone's goals for the future are to get his own apartment and a job. He hopes he can be a good father to his son someday. He's not sure how realistic these goals are.

Mental status: Although he seems mildly depressed, as evidenced by sad expression and a slumped posture in his chair, Mr. Stone's mental status seems normal and unremarkable.

Strengths: Mr. Stone is candid about his current condition. He related well to the interviewer. His health is good. He is verbal, has a sense of humor, and seems eager to please.

Weaknesses: History of several failed alcoholism treatments. Long history of alcoholic lifestyle; no long periods of work experience or skills. No current intimate involvements or other positive influences.

Stage of change: Mr. Stone is in either precontemplation or early contemplation.

Date: 1/1/09

Signed: Reginald Carter, CASAC

plation or contemplation. The reality of clinical work is that counselors are often not clear about some elements of client information. Therefore, be sure to indicate your degree of certainty. In Exhibit 13.2, note the question "What makes you think you have a drinking problem?" I often use this question when a client states that he or she has substance use problems. It is essentially an open question that allows the client to talk about his or her substance use problems and has the advantage of rarely engaging defensiveness.

Treatment Plans

Most treatment programs are required to prepare treatment plans for all of their clients. It usually falls to the substance abuse counselor to write them. The purpose of the treatment plan is to map out what the treatment will do for the client and how it will be done. A treatment plan should be individualized, laying out specific goals for the treatment, the kinds of interventions to be used, and how long it should take to achieve the goals. The principles of BSGS lend themselves to the philosophy of treatment plans. You have learned to think about goals for each session; now you can expand the time frame and think about goals for the long term. An important aspect of treatment plans is measuring whether the goals were met. Thus, goals should be measurable (see Exercise E.4.3).

Because assessment is an ongoing process, treatment plans must be modified over time. After modification, plans are typically called *revised treatment plans* or *treatment plan reviews*. The client's first treatment plan is, naturally, called the *initial treatment plan*. A *discharge* or *aftercare plan* summarizes the progress of the client in the treatment program and indicates the additional steps that need to be taken for the client to remain abstinent and well adjusted after he or she leaves the program.

I have found that reviewing the treatment plans with clients often leads to a productive and cooperative dialogue. Counselors and clients may have different views of the goals of the counseling and different priorities. Discussing the treatment plan provides a way to iron these differences out. Sometimes clients are not satisfied with progress the counselor thinks is very good, whereas other clients have difficulty acknowledging that they have not made very much progress, so a review of the treatment plan can provide an opportunity to discuss realistic benchmarks for progress.

An outline for making an initial treatment is provided in Exhibit 13.3; it is based on the psychosocial narrative of David Stone (see Exhibit 13.2). The problem list should include the major areas of concern in the client's recovery. Typically, these include use of alcohol and drugs, health issues, mental health issues, legal issues, family and marital issues, vocational issues, spiritual issues, and housing problems. *Goals* are derived from the specific problem list of the client; each problem cited should have a long-term goal. In David Stone's treatment plan, the first problem is alcohol dependence, and the goal derived from this problem is stable abstinence from alcohol and other drugs. Each goal should include at least one objective. An objective is a smaller goal that the counselor and client will work on during the current period of the treatment plan. The first objective for stable abstinence in this plan is to build motivation for treatment.

Next, the treatment plan notes the procedure for reaching this objective: reviewing previous treatment efforts. This is followed by the person responsible for conducting the procedure (in the example, Reginald Carter, CASAC) and the time frame (how long the procedure will take). The final item, "as measured by," indicates how to determine whether the objective was met. The rest of the treatment plan is constructed in a similar manner. (Antabuse, mentioned in Goal 1, Objective 3, is a medication that makes a person ill when he or she drinks and can serve as a deterrent to drinking. More information about Antabuse can be found in Yalisove, 2004, Chapter 3.)

An important consideration in drawing up a treatment plan is determining the best objectives for each goal during the time period under review. Just as we discussed in relation to BSGS, it is important to choose the appropriate objective: It should be relevant to the overall goal, achievable, and something the client signs on to. In some instances, it is appropriate to defer work on a goal or objective. For example, if a client is still drinking and in precontemplation, it is appropriate to defer vocational and educational goals.

> **Exhibit 13.3**
> **Developing a Treatment Plan Based on the**
> **Psychosocial Narrative of David Stone**
>
> Instructions are listed in italic type.
>
> *Step 1: Develop a problem list:*
>
> 1. Mr. Stone suffers from alcohol dependence (meets *DSM–IV–TR* Substance Dependence Criteria 1, 4, and 6).
> 2. He has no permanent housing.
> 3. He is unemployed.
> 4. He is socially isolated.
> 5. He has a history of previous failed treatment efforts.
> 6. He has had marginal health care in the past 5 years.
>
> *Step 2: Create a long-term goal for each of the problems:*
>
> Goal 1: Stable abstinence from alcohol and other psychoactive drugs
> Goal 2: Stable housing
> Goal 3: Gainful employment
> Goal 4: Positive social ties
> Goal 5: An effective treatment plan that takes into account previous failed treatment attempts
> Goal 6: Physical health
>
> *Step 3: Prioritize issues to be dealt with:*
>
> There are no urgent issues here, but the first concern is that Mr. Stone is alcohol dependent, with recent episodes of drinking. The first goal addresses this problem:
>
> ## Goal 1: Stable Abstinence From Alcohol and Other Psychoactive Drugs
>
> *Step 4: Break down each goal into objectives (smaller goals). Prioritize again:*
>
> **Objective 1:** Build motivation for treatment.
> *Each objective should have a treatment procedure; in this case:*
>
> *Procedure:* Assess previous treatment. Discuss good and not so good features of all previous treatments, and develop a description of the best treatment for the client.
> *Homework:* Client is to write about the pros and cons of his previous treatment.
> *Person responsible:* Reginald Carter, CASAC
> *Length of time:* 5 days
>
> *(Continued)*

Exhibit 13.3 *(Continued)*
Developing a Treatment Plan Based on the
Psychosocial Narrative of David Stone

As measured by: Client's completion of writing about previous treatment pros and cons.

The remainder of the treatment plan was constructed according to the same guidelines as above in Goal 1, Objective 1.

Objective 2: Participation in self-help groups.
Procedure: Explore the client's resistance to AA. Ask the client to detail his experiences in AA. Determine whether they are typical or unusual. Educate him about other ways to use AA. Discuss alternative self-help groups. Discuss ways he may use AA. Encourage participation in some self-help organization.
Person responsible: Reginald Carter, CASAC
Length of time: 28 days
As measured by: Attendance at at least five self-help meetings.

Objective 3: Education about Antabuse.
Procedure: Introduce the client to Antabuse through education and discussion. Referral to Maria Martinez, MD, for Antabuse. Client will begin taking Antabuse the week before discharge.
Person responsible: Reginald Carter, CASAC
Length of time: 28 days
As measured by: The client taking Antabuse in the counselor's presence.

Goal 2: Stable Housing

Objective 1: Facilitate referral to social services for a sober living house.
Procedure: Monitor the client's compliance with following through on application for housing.
Person responsible: Reginald Carter, CASAC
Length of time: 28 days
As measured by: Review of application, verification of appointments, and confirmation of client's admission to housing.

Goal 3: Gainful Employment

Objective 1: Encourage referral for vocational or educational guidance.
Procedure: Referral to one or both of the above.
Person responsible: Reginald Carter, CASAC
Length of time: 21 days

(Continued)

Exhibit 13.3 *(Continued)*
Developing a Treatment Plan Based on the
Psychosocial Narrative of David Stone

As measured by: Confirmed attendance at vocational counseling or education program.

Goal 4: Positive Social Ties

Objective 1: Encourage involvement in the program's recreation activities.
Procedure: Encourage involvement in self-help groups. Explore the possibility of developing positive leisure-time activities, including hobbies.
Person responsible: Reginald Carter, CASAC
Length of time: 28 days
As measured by: Attendance at social functions at rehab, self-help attendance, commitment to hobby and other leisure-time pursuits.

Goal 5: An Effective Treatment Plan That Takes Into Account Previous Failed Treatment Attempts

Objective 1: Build motivation for treatment.
Procedure: Assess the client's previous treatment. Discuss the good and not so good features of all previous treatments, and develop a description of the best treatment for the client.
Homework: Client should write about the pros and cons of his previous treatment.
Person responsible: Reginald Carter, CASAC
Length of time: 5 days
As measured by: Client's completion of homework.

Objective 2: Develop a treatment plan the client endorses.
Procedure: On the basis of the above assessment, tailor treatment, with the client's participation, to encourage his active, successful involvement in treatment.
Person responsible: Reginald Carter, CASAC
Length of time: 28 days
As measured by: Completion of a detailed treatment plan that the client endorses.

Goal 6: Physical Health

Objective 1: Assess the client's current physical health.
Procedure: Complete physical work-up.
Person responsible: Maria Martinez, MD

(Continued)

Exhibit 13.3 *(Continued)*
Developing a Treatment Plan Based on the
Psychosocial Narrative of David Stone

Length of time: 5 days
As measured by: All results recorded in chart.

Objective 2: Ensure compliance for proper medical follow-up.
Procedure: Review medical findings, and monitor compliance.
Person responsible: Maria Martinez, MD
Length of time: 28 days
As measured by: Recommended follow-up documented in chart.

Date: _2/1/09_
Signed by client: _David Stone_

Date: _2/1/09_
Signed by primary counselor: _Reginald Carter, CASAC_

Revised Treatment Plans

Periodically, typically every 3 months, each client's treatment plan must be reviewed and revised. I have created a discharge summary and aftercare plan (see Exhibit 13.4) from the rehabilitation unit David went to and a brief intake summary to the outpatient unit (see Exhibit 13.5) to provide enough information to create a revised treatment plan for David (see Exhibit 13.6).

One important feature of a revised treatment plan is an assessment of whether the goals were met in the previous treatment plan. If the objectives were not met, consideration should be given to why they were not met and how procedures or interventions can be modified to reach the objective in the new treatment plan. In the example, Mr. Stone has not become very involved in AA during the first treatment plan. In the revised plan, the counselor will explore in detail Mr. Stone's problems getting involved in AA and discuss other kinds of self-help groups. The counselor should review this plan with the client and problem solve the issues with him so that the client can collaborate in the creation of the revised treatment plan. It is not a good idea to repeat the same objective and treatment procedure for several revisions of the treatment plan. If progress is not being made on the objectives, the counselor and client should problem solve and revise them. If they have been achieved, new objectives and treatment procedures should be devised.

Progress Notes

Counselors must document their professional contacts with a client in the client's medical chart. This entry is typically called a progress note. The note need not be lengthy but should include the status of the client, the

---

Exhibit 13.4
Abbreviated Discharge Summary and
Aftercare Plan From Recovery Center Inpatient Unit

Discharge Summary

Mr. Stone was safely detoxified from alcohol and completed the inpatient treatment stay of 28 days. He is in good health, was active in all treatment groups, and attended the AA meetings in the facility. He did not, however, attend any of the AA meetings outside the facility. He has accepted that he has alcohol dependence and realizes that abstinence is the safest goal for him at this time. He began to take Antabuse while in the program and was given a prescription for it on discharge.

Mr. Stone attended vocational counseling sessions but was unable to develop a concrete plan regarding education or work on discharge.

Mr. Stone was somewhat isolated in relation to his peers and tended to shy away from socializing.

Aftercare Plan

Mr. Stone will begin outpatient treatment at the Recovery Center outpatient unit on discharge. He will be living at Sobriety House and has agreed to continue taking Antabuse.

Date: 2/28/09

Signed: Reginald Carter, CASAC

---

issues the counselor and client worked on, the outcome of the session, and the plan for continued work. The style of writing should be nonjudgmental and not too casual, specific in content, and relevant to substance abuse issues. A good way to keep track of what you need to write is to use a mnemonic in which each letter of the key word represents an element of the progress note. I learned *STOP.* This stands for *status* of the patient at the beginning of the session, *treatment* provided, *outcome,* and *plan.* Cameron and Turtle-Song (2002) discussed an alternative approach, called *SOAP* (subjective, objective, assessment, and plan). Other approaches that use mnemonics to guide counselors in crafting their progress notes can be found in Cournoyer (2005, pp. 406–409).

Exhibit 13.7 gives an example of a progress note imagined for David Stone in an outpatient clinic visit; the example uses the STOP format. Progress notes should include the date of the visit and the kind of service provided and should be signed by the counselor with his or her profes-

---

Exhibit 13.5
Abbreviated Intake Summary at Recovery Center
Outpatient Unit

Mr. Stone appeared at his scheduled interview at the outpatient unit. He seemed cooperative but mildly depressed. He stated that he wished to remain abstinent and, to that end, will continue to take Antabuse. He is less eager to attend AA meetings. He complained of having been lonely and isolated since he left the rehab facility. He also stated that he had no ideas regarding his vocational or educational goals but said he would prefer to work as soon as possible.

Date: <u>3/1/09</u>

Signed: <u>Rebecca Smith, CASAC</u>

---

sional credential (CASAC is the credential for alcoholism and substance abuse counselors in New York), as shown in Exhibit 13.7. Ideally, the progress note should refer to the goals and objectives set out in the treatment plan. In this note, reference is made to AA attendance, which is an objective in the treatment plan.

Paperwork is a necessary function of the job for all counselors. Your supervisor and the clinic director will appreciate it if you keep up to date on the work, write legibly, and use a clear writing style. Develop a routine at work so you can organize your paperwork assignments and avoid falling behind. Although counselors may tend just to have clients sign off where required, as on treatment plans, I have always found it useful to explain carefully what the purpose of the document is, be sure the client understands what it says, and determine whether he or she agrees with the content. One rule of thumb in clinical writing is to write as if the client were looking over your shoulder. This will help you write nonjudgmentally and determine whether you have a good working relationship with your client.

The examples in this chapter are meant to give you an understanding of clinical writing. The actual format of treatment plans and other clinical writing varies from agency to agency. Be sure you follow the format and style of the guidelines provided by the agency you work for.

Exercises

E.13.1. Progress Notes

Examples of progress notes appear on pages 159–160. Underline good and bad features of these notes and explain. Place STOP elements in the examples, using the first letter in parentheses.

| Exhibit 13.6 |
| Revised Treatment Plan for David Stone |

Problem areas:

Alcohol dependence with
  short remission periods
Social isolation
Lack of vocational plan

Goals:

Stable abstinence from
  alcohol and other drugs
Sober support system
Gainful employment

Progress in last treatment plan: Mr. Stone completed all of the required elements of his initial treatment plan, including detoxification and use of Antabuse. He made only modest progress, however, in his AA involvement and in developing plans to become employed.

Goal 1: Stable Abstinence From Alcohol and Other Drugs

Objective 1: Continue Antabuse therapy.
Procedure: Client will continue taking Antabuse, prescribed by Maria Martinez, MD.
Person responsible: Rebecca Smith, CASAC
Length of time: 28 days
As measured by: Client's taking Antabuse in the primary counselor's presence.

Objective 2: Explore the client's resistance to self-help.
Procedure: Ask the client to detail his experiences in AA. Determine whether they are typical or unusual. Educate him about other ways to use AA. Discuss alternative self-help groups. Discuss ways he may use them. Encourage participation in some self-help organization.
Person responsible: Rebecca Smith, CASAC
Length of time: 28 days
As measured by: Attendance at at least five self-help meetings.

Objective 3: Prevent relapse.
Procedure: Develop a list of relapse triggers. Develop strategies to prevent relapse. Role-play possible danger situations.
Person responsible: Rebecca Smith, CASAC
Length of time: 90 days
As measured by: Client's confidence that he can deal with relapse triggers.

Goal 2: Sober Support System

Objective 1: Explore difficulties involved in developing social contacts.

(Continued)

Exhibit 13.6 *(Continued)*
Revised Treatment Plan for David Stone

Procedure: Individual counseling.
Person responsible: Rebecca Smith, CASAC
Length of time: 90 days
As measured by: Creation of a detailed list of difficulties and steps to overcome them.

Objective 2: Implement a plan of small steps toward increased socializing.
Procedure: Individual counseling
Person responsible: Rebecca Smith, CASAC
Length of time: 90 days
As measured by: Participation in social activities in the community.

Goal 3: Gainful Employment

Objective 1: Refer the client to vocational counseling, and monitor his attendance.
Procedure: Individual counseling.
Person responsible: Rebecca Smith, CASAC
Length of time: 90 days
As measured by: Attendance at vocational counseling sessions.

Date: _3/5/09_
Signed by client: _David Stone_

Date: _3/5/09_
Signed by primary counselor: _Reginald Carter, CASAC_

---

a. 12/12/08. *Individual counseling session.* Cathy came to her session enthusiastic about a possible sponsor she met at an AA meeting last night. She reported having been abstinent for 1 month as of yesterday. Counselor reviewed the desirable characteristics of a sponsor with Cathy and suggested that she meet with the potential sponsor a few more times to see whether the woman would make a good sponsor. Cathy agreed that this was a good idea and said she would meet Anna, the potential sponsor, for coffee after the meetings they both attend. Individual appointment set for next week. *(Signed)* Sarah McBride, CASAC.

b. 1/9/09. *Group session.* Michelle was so late for her session that we couldn't accomplish anything. The other group members confronted her. I told her if she wasn't more motivated, she would be terminated from the program. *(Signed)* Richard Daly, CASAC.

> **Exhibit 13.7**
> **Progress Note for David Stone**
> _____
>
> *3/15/09.* Individual counseling session.
>
> *Status.* David has now been abstinent 41 days. He just attended his first AA meeting since his discharge from the rehab. He said he felt nervous and out of place but was glad he went.
>
> *Treatment.* We discussed which meeting he had attended, what made him nervous, and ways of overcoming this nervousness. I said that it was great that he had made this very positive step and encouraged him to attend an additional meeting before our next session.
>
> *Outcome.* He smiled when I said he had taken a positive step and said that he was sure that he would attend at least one meeting before our next session.
>
> *Plan.* Individual appointment set for next week.
>
> —Rebecca Smith, CASAC

  c. *4/14/09. Individual session.* Michael said he hated "spics" because they were so dishonest. I told him that he was a bigot and that unless he stopped talking like that, I couldn't be his counselor. *(Signed)* Evelyn Cantor, CASAC.

  d. *5/9/09. Family session.* Everyone participated and was pleased with Clem's progress. *(Signed)* Joan Pollyanna, CASAC.

  e. *6/8/09. Individual session.* Sebastian has a new girlfriend. He is in love. He wouldn't go into any details about her. I asked him about her attitudes about drinking and taking drugs; he refused to say. *(Signed)* Tom Jones, CASAC.

E.13.2. Using Elements of STOP

Take dialogues created in earlier team role-play exercises and create a progress note for them. Be sure all of the elements in STOP are included.

E.13.3. Creating Treatment Plans

Create an initial and revised treatment plan based on a case study. For the revised treatment plan, you will have to create (i.e., make up) the progress of the first phase of treatment. If your team has used the case study of one client as he or she progresses through treatment, you may use this. You must summarize his or her progress (or lack thereof) as a part of the written assignment. Each team member should role-play a counselor discussing these treatment plans with a team member who role-plays the client. This will be a part of the workbook log. Be sure that the observers keep a detailed record of the dialogue. Remember to set goals and techniques before beginning the role-play.

Chapter 14

Closing Perspective

I hope you have enjoyed this brief introduction to substance abuse coun-seling skills. This is just the beginning of your professional development; let me make a few suggestions about continuing it. First, you can hone the skills you have learned in this book. By using the three-step BSGS process, you can reflect on your skills and seek to improve them. In addition, you should learn some additional skills (e.g., working with adolescents) that are not presented in this book. It is also important to familiarize yourself with substance abuse counseling theory and addiction research findings to increase your understanding of addictive disorders. Another important area of professional development is understanding and abiding by profes-sional ethics. But before I discuss these areas, let me give you some advice about surviving your first job in substance abuse counseling.

Survival at Your First Job

On the positive side, if you have good skills, you should have little diffi-culty getting a job in the substance abuse field. On the negative side, many agencies are underfunded, understaffed, and plagued by other problems. Additionally, some agencies subscribe to a specific treatment ideology that is mandatory for all counselors. Not all agencies endorse the principles I have laid out in this book. For example, if you are a harm reduction advo-cate, you will not fit into most therapeutic communities, where abstinence is typically the only acceptable goal. Thus, it makes sense to get a good idea of an agency before you accept a position there.

A prime consideration for your first job should be obtaining good-quality supervision. No matter how much you learn in your classes, your supervisor can provide invaluable guidance in applying that learning. Because the quality of supervision varies among agencies, I recommend that you meet with your prospective supervisor and see whether you would feel comfortable working with him or her before accepting a position. Consider the following, for example:

- Is the potential supervisor respectful of you?
- Will you get sufficient supervision time?
- Will you be given specific guidance on the issues you need to work on?
- Do you know the supervisor's credentials, training, experience, and theoretical point of view?
- Is he or she a competent substance abuse counselor?
- Will he or she be helpful in improving your counseling skills?
- Is he or she qualified to serve as your supervisor, given your state credentialing requirements? (In New York State, e.g., the supervisor has to be a qualified mental health professional—i.e., CASAC, licensed psychologist, counselor, social worker, nurse, or physician.)

Supervisors sometimes ask clinical staff to work overtime, to take on heavy caseloads, and to perform functions beyond their competence. It is hard to fault them for making these requests because of the funding realities of substance abuse agencies. Conversely, you must protect yourself and respectfully decline duties that you are uncomfortable performing.

Although I believe the principles and skills laid out in this book should be helpful in most substance abuse agencies, you may have to modify them for a variety of reasons. One reason, as mentioned above, is that the agency may have a set theory and technique that all staff must follow. Another is that the nature of the client population serviced by the agency may have special features that make some of the techniques set out in this book less than optimal. It makes sense to modify your technique to fit the specific demands of the clinical situations you must work with. I do, however, urge you to work with integrity. That is, if you are convinced that specific principles that are essential for good care are not in operation at an agency you are working at, you may need to leave that agency.

Burnout

Burnout refers to the psychological exhaustion that may set in when counselors must work with challenging clients under difficult conditions. As you can see from reading this book, counseling substance-abusing clients is quite challenging. A few suggestions may help you cope:

- Good supervision will help you learn how to provide more effective interventions, keep perspective about your role in your client's treatment, and maintain appropriate boundaries and will give you encouragement.
- Programs that have adequate resources and a treatment philosophy suited to the client population will make work collaborative and less stressful.
- Sharing concerns in self-help groups and in your own individual counseling can help as well.

Continuing Your Education

This book is intended to give the new counselor only the most basic skills for substance abuse counseling. Additional skills, knowledge, and theory are essential if you want to develop into a master counselor. The following sections list additional substance abuse counseling topics, along with some recommended resources.

Professional Ethics

Counselors have special ethical responsibilities because they affect clients' lives. These special responsibilities are reflected in the code of ethics of NAADAC, the Association for Addiction Professionals. The basic elements of the code include the following:

- Counselors must treat all clients and colleagues fairly and without discrimination. Counselors must treat all clients with diligence, regardless of the client's cultural or ethnic background, and respect cultural differences. They must make appropriate accommodations to treatment given the cultural practices of the client. (Diversity and multicultural counseling are discussed more fully in Chapter 12.)
- Counselors must maintain professional competence and provide only those services for which they are fully educated and trained (i.e., scope of practice). When counselors become impaired through the use of alcohol or other drugs or for other reasons, they are ethically bound to limit their contact with clients so that the clients' treatment is not negatively affected.
- Counselors may not engage in dual relationships with clients. That is, they may not become romantically involved with clients, have business relationships with them, or become their AA or NA sponsors. Such interactions compromise the therapeutic relationship.
- In counseling relationships, the client's freedom to choose (i.e., autonomy) should be respected whenever possible. Thus, clients must be fully informed about their disorders, the nature of the treatments they are being offered, and all other relevant provisions of service. Then they must freely consent to the procedures recommended (i.e., informed consent).

- Additionally, counselors must adhere to certain state and federal laws that pertain to counseling. All mental health counselors are bound by the requirement to report suspected child abuse and neglect. In instances in which clients are likely to harm a specific person, counselors have a "duty to warn." Clients treated in substance abuse facilities have legal protection regarding confidentiality. Although there are exceptions, such as the two noted above, for the most part, information about clients can only be released with their written permission.

The complete NAADAC code of ethics may be found on the Web (NAADAC, the Association for Addiction Professionals, 2008).

Equally important, you should learn and understand the ethical principles of counseling. Most of these issues are covered in the American Counseling Association's (2005) *ACA Code of Ethics*. I also recommend Welfel (2006) for information about professional ethics.

Working With Adolescents

It takes special skills to work with adolescents. The Center for Substance Abuse Treatment (2003) offers good information about working with adolescents with substance abuse disorders. Keep in mind that to become proficient in clinical skill areas such as this, you must follow book knowledge and course knowledge with a sufficient amount of supervision by an expert in the area (W. R. Miller, Sorensen, Selzer, & Brigham, 2006).

Research Knowledge in Substance Abuse

Research knowledge about addiction is growing rapidly, and new approaches to managing addictive illness are being developed. It is essential to keep up to date on this new knowledge. An introduction to the addiction literature is presented in *Introduction to Alcohol Research* (Yalisove, 2004). With rich Web resources available now, you can also go to reliable Web sites for the latest research findings. The following are three good places to start:

- The National Institute on Alcoholism and Alcohol Abuse is the federal agency that supports research, prevention, and treatment for alcohol disorders. Its Web address is www.niaaa.nih.gov/.
- The National Institute on Drug Addiction is the federal agency that supports research, prevention, and treatment for drug use disorders. Its Web address is www.nida.nih.gov/.
- Addiction Treatment Technology Transfer Centers are federally funded regional centers that disseminate knowledge about alcohol and substance use disorders. Their Web address is www.nattc.org/.

Theories of Substance Abuse Counseling

A theory of counseling is an organized view of addiction that provides an explanation for its causes and a systematic approach to its treatment. Theories are often very convincing, but they may not have scientific support. I have listed the most popular theories in addiction treatment in the following sections.

Twelve-step facilitation. Because 12-step facilitation is based on the principles of AA, I recommend that substance abuse counselors read AA and NA literature. The most popular books are the following:

Alcoholics Anonymous World Services. (1976). *Alcoholics Anonymous.* New York: Author.

This book sets out the principles of AA. AA members refer to it as the "Big Book."

Alcoholics Anonymous World Services. (1981). *Twelve steps and twelve traditions.* New York: Author.

This brief book explains what the 12 steps of AA mean and how members can use them. It also details the 12 traditions, which are the principles by which the organization runs.

Center for Substance Abuse Treatment. (1995). *Twelve step facilitation therapy manual* (National Institute on Alcohol Abuse and Alcoholism Project MATCH Monograph Series, Vol. 1; NIH Publication No. 94-3722). Rockville, MD: U.S. Department of Health and Human Services, Public Health Service, National Institutes of Health.

This good manual of 12-step facilitation was developed as a part of the Project MATCH research study.

Narcotics Anonymous World Service Office. (1988). *Narcotics Anonymous.* Van Nuys, CA: Author.

This is the main text for NA.

Hazelden, the organization that pioneered 12-step treatment, offers many publications that develop the 12-step point of view for addiction treatment. Hazelden also provides access to free databases of articles about addiction. Its Web site is www.hazelden.org/.

Cognitive–behavioral approaches to addiction treatment. Cognitive–behavioral treatment is by far the most researched treatment for addictions. The following are some resources on this important approach to treating addiction:

Center for Substance Abuse Treatment. (1995). *Cognitive behavioral coping skills therapy manual* (National Institute on Alcohol Abuse and Alcoholism Project MATCH Monograph Series, Vol. 1, NIH Publication No. 94-3724). Rockville, MD: U.S. Department of Health and Human Services, Public Health Service, National Institutes of Health.

This manual was developed as part of the Project MATCH research study.

Hester, R. K., & Miller, W. R. (Eds.). (2003). *Handbook of alcoholism treatment approaches: Effective alternatives* (3rd ed.). New York: Allyn & Bacon.
This book covers all of the important CBT interventions used to treat substance abuse.

Monti, P. M., Kadden, R. M., Rohsenow, D. J., Cooney, N. L., & Abrams, D. B. (2002). *Treating alcohol dependence: A coping skills training guide.* New York: Guilford Press.
This work is a practical guide to conducting coping skills training in substance abuse treatment settings.

MI. Although MI is featured in this book, its principles and techniques go beyond what I have presented. The first places to go for more information are the following:

Center for Substance Abuse Treatment. (1995). *Motivational enhancement therapy manual* (National Institute on Alcohol Abuse and Alcoholism Project MATCH Monograph Series, Vol. 2, NIH Publication No. 94-3723). Rockville, MD: U.S. Department of Health and Human Services, Public Health Service, National Institutes of Health.
This manual was also developed for the Project MATCH research study.

Center for Substance Abuse Treatment. (1999). *Enhancing motivation for change in substance use disorder treatment* (Treatment Improvement Protocol Series 35, DHHS Publication No. SMA 99-3354). Rockville, MD: Substance Abuse and Mental Health Services Administration.
This manual provides a concise and readable account of MI.

Miller, W. R., & Rollnick, S. (1991, 2002). *Motivational interviewing: Preparing people for change.* New York: Guilford Press.
The creators of MI wrote this book. The first edition, published in 1991, is more informal and reader friendly. The second edition presents more research and innovations for MI. I recommend them both.

For training in MI, you can contact the Motivational Interviewing Network of Trainers at http://motivationalinterviewing.org/.

Common factors theory. The theoretical orientation of this book is common factors theory. The following two books do a good job of presenting this point of view:

Hubble, M. A., Duncan, B. L., & Miller, S. D. (Eds.). (1999). *The heart and soul of change: What works in therapy.* Washington, DC: American Psychological Association.
Norcross, J. (Ed.). (2002). *Psychotherapy relationships that work.* New York: Oxford University Press.

All of the government publications listed above (both National Institutes of Health publications and Department of Health and Human Services publications), as well as many other government publications, are available for free or at low cost from the Substance Abuse and Mental Health Services Administration (http://ncadistore.samhsa.gov/catalog/). Many of the publications can be downloaded or ordered in hard copy.

Obtaining Your Substance Abuse Counseling Credential

In the United States, each state regulates credentials for addiction counseling. At the current time, rapid changes are occurring in the certification process. You should contact your state's substance abuse treatment department for details. In New York State, for example, students should contact the Office of Alcoholism and Substance Abuse Services. The Addiction Treatment Technology Transfer Center Web site (www.nattc.org/) provides links to the agencies in each state that regulate credentials for substance abuse counseling. The International Certification & Reciprocity Consortium (www.icrcaoda.org/) sets standards of practice in addiction counseling. Although standards vary from state to state, many states follow the consortium's standards, which require

- a minimum of 270 hours of education, of which 6 must be specific to ethics;
- 6,000 hours of supervised work experience at a state-licensed substance abuse treatment agency (credit for 2,000 hours can be granted for obtaining a bachelor's degree in the behavioral sciences, and credit for 4,000 hours can be granted for obtaining a master's degree in the behavioral sciences);
- 300 hours of supervision addressing the core functions of substance abuse counseling;
- a successfully passed written examination;
- a signed code of ethics statement; and
- 40 hours of continuing education completed every 2 years after credentialing.

Most states' standards are reflected in the above requirements, but individual states may require more educational hours (e.g., New York State requires 350 hours) and may require additional specific content (e.g., New York State requires 45 hours related to professional and ethical responsibilities). There is some reciprocity among states. See the International Certification & Reciprocity Consortium Web site for details.

Professional Organizations for Substance Abuse Counselors

NAADAC, the Association for Addiction Professionals, is the national organization for substance abuse counselors. Its Web site is http://naadac.org/. The International Association of Addictions and Offender Counselors is a division of the American Counseling Association. Its Web site is www.iaaoc.org.

Answer Guide

This guide gives answers to some of the chapter exercises.

Chapter 3: Some Basic Principles of Substance Abuse Counseling

E.3.1. Develop a rationale for an intervention (e.g., psychiatric referral, detoxification, psychiatric medication, specialized treatment for PTSD, participation in AA or NA) or treatment approach (e.g., methadone maintenance treatment program, therapeutic community, MI, or CBT).

Answer: Rationale for participation in AA or NA: "AA and NA are self-help groups that have helped more people get sober than any other way. There are thousands of meetings to choose from. There is no cost. People who have had problems similar to yours have found a way to get sober, and they will offer their practical suggestions and support to help you. How does this sound to you? Would you be willing to try it?"

Chapter 4: Applying the Principles of Building Session Goals and Strategies (BSGS) to Prepare for a Session With a Client

E.4.2. Develop a goal and techniques for the following scenarios:

a. The patient is resistant to attending AA or NA.
b. The client becomes depressed.
c. The client reports "drink signals" (i.e., the client is afraid he or she might drink).
d. The client becomes homeless.
e. The client starts a romantic relationship.
f. The client wants to leave treatment prematurely and try change on his or her own.
g. The client is noncompliant (e.g., misses sessions, is chronically late, or does not do homework).

Answer to 4.2.a: The overall goal is to help the client develop sober supportive relationships. This may not necessarily mean attendance at AA or NA meetings.

Techniques:

1. Explore resistance. There may be a good reason for the client's resistance. Perhaps you are pushing too soon for attendance. Has the client ever attended AA or NA? What was his or her experience? Does he or she have some misconceptions about AA and NA?
2. Offer education. Many clients do not know anything about AA and NA or have misconceptions about the programs. That is an important reason for all substance abuse counselors to have a thorough knowledge and understanding of AA and NA.
3. Break the goal into small steps: Ask the client to attend one meeting or read some AA or NA literature, then discuss it with him or her.
4. Provide information about other self-help groups, and discuss involvement in one of them.

Answer to E.4.2.g: The goal is to restore compliance.

Techniques:

1. Assess the client's motivation for change.
2. Problem solve with the client.
3. Review the goals for treatment to be sure you and the client agree.
4. Remind the client of the consequences (if any) of noncompliance.

E.4.3. What are some ways of objectively measuring the goals you developed for the scenarios in E.4.2 by the end of the session and over a period of time? List additional goals and how they can be measured.

Answer to E.4.3.a: The patient's resistance can be measured by the number of AA or NA meetings he or she attends per week.

Answer to E.4.3.g: If the client's attendance has been an issue, success can be measured as better attendance. If the client has been late, success can be measured as better on-time performance.

Chapter 5: Building Session Goals and Strategies (BSGS) and the First Session

E.5.1. Compose your opening statement for a new client. Role-play it with your partner. He or she should react to it. Be sure that the observers keep a detailed record.

Answer: Opening statement: "Hi, I'm Dr. Yalisove. Please have a seat and make yourself comfortable. Today we're going to meet for about 45 minutes to see whether our clinic can be of help to you. I'll be asking you some questions to figure that out. Okay? So, tell me, what brings you here today?"

E.5.3. What do you think a client coming to a substance abuse counseling center expects on the first visit? Take a few minutes to consider this; put yourself in the shoes of a client coming to a counseling session for the first time. What would a reasonable client anticipate? What might he or she expect from a first visit to a substance abuse counselor? Write down your reactions.

Answer: A client would expect to be asked about drugs and alcohol. He or she would expect to be treated respectfully. He or she would expect the counselor to have expertise, answer questions, and offer help.

E.5.4.b. Role-play: Administer the AUDIT (Babor et al., 2001) and give feedback. (See Center for Substance Abuse Treatment, 1999, pp. 65–71, for suggestions on how to give feedback in MI style.) Before doing so, be clear about your goals. What are they? What techniques will you use? Role-play this exercise with your partner. He or she should react to your feedback. This will be a part of the workbook log. Be sure that the observer keeps a detailed record. When doing the role-play, give the client the following rationale for using the AUDIT modified for use in a substance abuse clinic:

> I am going to ask you some questions about your use of alcohol during the past year. To determine whether you need treatment for alcoholism and, if so, what kind of treatment, it is important for us to know how much you usually drink and whether you have experienced any problems with your drinking. Please try to be as honest and as accurate as you can be.

Answer regarding goals and techniques:
Goals:
1. Obtain objective information to help evaluate the client's alcohol use.
2. Raise the client's awareness and build his or her motivation to change regarding his or her alcohol use.

Techniques:
1. Accurately administer the AUDIT according to the guidelines for objective comparison with other drinkers.
2. Deliver the results objectively and nonjudgmentally.
3. Ask for the client's reaction to the results.

E.5.7. Which of the following are open questions and closed questions?

Answers:
a. Is this a closed question? Closed.
b. Is this an open question? Closed.
c. How does marijuana fit into your daily life? Open.

d. Are you happy with your use of cocaine? Closed.

e. What brings you here today? Open.

f. How much alcohol do you typically drink every day? Closed.

Chapter 6: Beyond the First Session: The Beginning Phase of Treatment

E.6.2. A client is actively using drugs but feels that his current job is causing the pressure that makes him use. He intends to seek a job with less pressure. You feel that he is not able to make a good decision while still actively using drugs. What would be your first goal with this client? What strategies and techniques would you use? This will be a part of the workbook log.

Answer: Goal: To have the client defer his decision.

Techniques:

1. Create a decisional balance listing the pros and cons of staying in and leaving the current job.

2. Problem solve ways to reduce pressure at the job.

3. Suggest that the client defer his decision until he has been abstinent 90 days.

Chapter 8: Moving Toward Termination

E.8.2. Some clients are in contemplation, determination, or action when treatment must be terminated. What goals should the counselor focus on for clients in these stages of change? Role-play a client in the last session in contemplation, determination, or action; one person role-plays the counselor. This will be a part of the workbook log. Be sure that the observers keep a detailed record of the dialogue. The team should discuss the goals and techniques to be used before beginning the role-play.

Answer: The chapter gives an example of a client leaving treatment in contemplation. The counselor's goal in the example is to help the client move from contemplation to determination—that is, make a decision about his marijuana use.

Chapter 13: Treatment Plans and Clinical Writing

E.13.1. Examples of progress notes appear on pages 159–160. Underline good and bad features of these notes and explain. Place STOP elements in the examples, using the first letter in parentheses.

Answer: All of the necessary elements of a progress note are present in example a:

12/12/08. *Individual counseling session.* (S) Cathy came to her session enthusiastic about a possible sponsor she met at an AA meeting last night. (S) She reported having been abstinent for 1 month as of yesterday. (T) Counselor reviewed the desirable characteristics of a sponsor with Cathy and (P) suggested that she meet with the potential sponsor a few more times to see whether the woman would make a good sponsor. (O) Cathy agreed that this was a good idea and said she would meet Anna, the potential sponsor, for coffee after the meetings they both attend. (P) Individual appointment set for next week. *(Signed)* Sarah McBride, CASAC.

The progress note in example b has several problems:

1/9/09. *Group session.* (S) Michelle was so late for her session that we couldn't accomplish anything. (T) The other group members confronted her. (T) I told her if she wasn't more motivated, she would be terminated from the program. *(Signed)* Richard Daly, CASAC.

No outcome or plan is mentioned in the note. The status of the client is incomplete. The note does not mention whether Michelle has been abstinent, and the description of the treatment provided is vague. The actual intervention seems to be too harsh.

References

American Counseling Association. (2005). *ACA code of ethics*. Alexandria, VA: Author.

American Psychiatric Association. (2000). *Diagnostic and statistical manual of mental disorders* (4th ed., text rev.). Washington, DC: Author.

Arnkoff, D. B., Glass, C. R., & Shapiro, S. J. (2002). Expectations and preferences. In J. C. Norcross (Ed.), *Psychotherapy relationships that work: Therapist contributions and responsiveness to patients* (pp. 335–356). New York: Oxford University Press.

Babor, T. F., Biddle, J. C., Saunders, J. B., & Monteiro, M. G. (2001). *AUDIT: Alcohol Use Disorders Identification Test: Guidelines for use in primary care* (2nd ed). Retrieved January 30, 2009, from http://whqlibdoc.who.int/hq/2001/WHO_MSD_MSB_01.6a.pdf

Belding, M. A., Iguchi, M. Y., Morral, A. R., & McLellan, A. T. (1997). Assessing the helping alliance and its impact in the treatment of opiate dependence. *Drug and Alcohol Dependence, 48,* 51–59.

Bell, D. C., Montoya, I. D., & Atkinson, J. S. (1997). Therapeutic connection and client progress in drug abuse treatment. *Journal of Clinical Psychology, 53,* 215–224.

Bien, T. H., Miller, W. R., & Tonnigan, J. S. (1993). Brief interventions for alcohol problems: A review. *Addiction, 88,* 315–336.

BigFoot, D. S., & Dunlap, M. (2006). Storytelling as a healing tool for American Indians. In T. M. Witko (Ed.), *Mental health care for urban Indians: Clinical insights from Native practitioners* (pp. 133–153). Washington, DC: American Psychological Association.

Bohart, A. C., Elliott, R., Greenberg, L. S., & Watson, J. C. (2002). Empathy. In J. Norcross (Ed.), *Psychotherapy relationships that work: Therapist contributions and responsiveness to patients* (pp. 89–108). New York: Oxford University Press.

Bostic, J. Q., Shadid, L. D., & Blotcky, M. J. (1996). Our time is up: Forced terminations during psychotherapy training. *American Journal of Psychotherapy, 50,* 347–359.

Boylin, W. M., Doucette, J., & Jean, M. F. (1997). Multifamily therapy in substance abuse treatment with women. *American Journal of Family Therapy, 25,* 39–47.

Brinson, J. A., Brew, L., & Denby, R. (2008). Real scenarios and complementary lectures: A classroom training approach to increase counselor awareness, knowledge, and skills. *Journal of Counseling & Development, 86,* 11–17.

Brogan, M. M., Prochaska, J. O., & Prochaska, J. M. (1999). Predicting termination and continuation status in psychotherapy using the transtheoretical model. *Psychotherapy, 36,* 105–113.

Burckell, L. A., & Goldfried, M. R. (2006). Therapist qualities preferred by sexual minority individuals. *Psychotherapy Theory, Research, Practice, Training, 43,* 32–49.

Burke, A. C., & Gregoire, T. K. (2007). Substance abuse treatment outcomes. *Health and Social Work, 32,* 7–15.

Cameron, S., & Turtle-Song, I. (2002). Learning to write case notes using the SOAP format. *Journal of Counseling & Development, 80,* 286–292.

Cartwright, B. Y., Daniels, J., & Zhang, S. (2008). Assessing multicultural competence: Perceived versus demonstrated performance. *Journal of Counseling & Development, 86,* 318–322.

Center for Substance Abuse Treatment. (1999). *Enhancing motivation for change in substance use disorder treatment* (Treatment Improvement Protocol Series 35, DHHS Publication No. SMA 99-3354). Rockville, MD: Substance Abuse and Mental Health Services Administration.

Center for Substance Abuse Treatment. (2000a). *A cognitive-behavioral approach: Treating cocaine addiction* (NIDA NIH Publication No. 00-4308). Bethesda, MD: U.S. Department of Health and Human Services, National Institutes of Health, National Institute on Drug Abuse.

Center for Substance Abuse Treatment. (2000b). *Substance abuse treatment for persons with HIV/AIDS* (Technical Assistance Publication Series 37, DHHS Publication No. SMA 08-4137). Rockville, MD: Substance Abuse and Mental Health Services Administration.

Center for Substance Abuse Treatment. (2003). *Therapy manuals for drug addiction: Manual 5: Brief strategic family therapy for adolescent drug abuse* (NIH Publication No. 03-4751). Rockville, MD: U.S. Department of Health and Human Services, Public Health Service, National Institutes of Health.

Center for Substance Abuse Treatment. (2005a). *Medication-assisted treatment for opioid addiction in opioid treatment programs* (Treatment Improvement Protocol Series 43, DHHS Publication No. SMA 05-4048). Retrieved August 4, 2009, from www.ncbi.nlm.nih.gov/books/bv.fcgi?rid=hstat5.chapter.82676

Center for Substance Abuse Treatment. (2005b). *Substance abuse treatment for adults in the criminal justice system* (Technical Assistance Publication Series 44, DHHS Publication No. SMA 05-4056). Rockville, MD: Substance Abuse and Mental Health Services Administration.

Center for Substance Abuse Treatment. (2005c). *Substance abuse treatment for persons with co-occurring disorders* (Treatment Improvement Protocol Series 42, DHHS Publication No. SMA 05-3922). Retrieved August 8, 2009, from www.ncbi.nlm.nih.gov/books/bv.fcgi?rid=hstat5.chapter.74073

Center for Substance Abuse Treatment. (2006). *Addiction counseling competencies: The knowledge, skills, and attitudes of professional practice* (Technical Assistance Publication Series 21, DHHS Publication No. SMA 06-4171). Rockville, MD: Substance Abuse and Mental Health Services Administration.

Cheng, Z. (2003). Issues and standards in counseling lesbians and gay men with substance abuse concerns. *Journal of Mental Health Counseling, 25,* 323–336.

Chow, J. (2002). Asian American and Pacific Islander mental health and substance abuse agencies: Organizational characteristics and service gaps. *Administration and Policy in Mental Health, 30,* 79–86.

Corey, G. (1981). *Theory/practice of group counseling.* Belmont, CA: Brooks/Cole.

Cork, M. (1969). *The forgotten children.* Toronto, Canada: Addiction Research Foundation.

Cournoyer, B. R. (2005). *Social work skills workbook.* Belmont, CA: Thomson, Brooks/Cole.

Drake, R. E., Bartels, S. J., Teague, B. E., Noordsy, D. L., & Clark, R. E. (1993). Treatment of substance abuse in severely mentally ill patients. *Journal of Nervous and Mental Disease, 181,* 606–611.

Flores, P. (1997). *Group psychotherapy with addicted populations.* Binghamton, NY: Haworth Press.

Forsyth, D. (1999). *Group dynamics* (3rd ed.). Belmont, CA: Brooks/Cole.

French, L. A. (2004). Alcohol and other drug addictions among Native Americans: The movement toward tribal-centric treatment programs. *Alcoholism Treatment Quarterly, 22,* 81–91.

Fuentes, J. N., Stracuzzi, T. I., Bennett, J., Scheinholtz, J., Hersh, M., Cheng, D., et al. (2006). Therapist multicultural competency: A study of therapist dyads. *Psychotherapy Theory, Research, Practice, Training, 43,* 480–490.

Gone, J. P. (2006). Mental health, wellness, and the quest for an authentic American Indian identity. In T. M. Witko (Ed.), *Mental health care for urban Indians: Clinical insights from Native practitioners* (pp. 55–80). Washington, DC: American Psychological Association.

Greenfield, L., Burgdorf, K., Chen, X., Porowski, A., Roberts, T., & Herrell, J. (2004). Effectiveness of long-term residential substance abuse treatment for women: Findings from three national studies. *American Journal of Drug and Alcohol Abuse, 30,* 537–550.

Haug, N. A., Sorensen, J. L., Gruber, V. A., & Song, S. (2005). Relapse prevention for opioid dependence. In G. A. Marlatt & D. M. Donovan (Eds.), *Relapse prevention: Maintenance strategies in the treatment of addictive behaviors* (2nd ed., pp. 151–178). New York: Guilford Press.

Hill, C. E., & Knox, S. (2002). Self-disclosure. In J. C. Norcross (Ed.), *Psychotherapy relationships that work: Therapist contributions and responsiveness to patients* (pp. 255–265). New York: Oxford University Press.

Horvath, A. O., & Bedi, R. P. (2002). The alliance. In J. C. Norcross (Ed.), *Psychotherapy relationships that work: Therapist contributions and responsiveness to patients* (pp. 37–69). New York: Oxford University Press.

Hubble, M. A., Duncan, B. L., & Miller, S. D. (1999). Directing attention to what works. In M. A. Hubble, B. L. Duncan, & S. D. Miller (Eds.), *The heart and soul of change: What works in therapy* (pp. 407–447). Washington, DC: American Psychological Association.

Hunsley, J., Aubry, T. D., & Verstervelt, C. M. (1999). Comparing therapist and client perspectives on reasons for psychotherapy terminations. *Psychotherapy, 36*, 380–388.

Jackson, J. (1954). The adjustment of the family to the crisis of alcoholism. *Quarterly Journal of Studies on Alcohol, 15*, 562–586.

Jacobson, J. O. (2004). Place and attrition from substance abuse treatment. *Journal of Drug Issues, 34*, 23–50.

Jarvis, T. J., Tebbutt, J., Mattick, R. P., & Shand, F. (2005). *Treatment approaches for alcohol and drug dependence: An introductory guide.* Hoboken, NJ: Wiley.

Joe, G. W., Simpson, D. D., Dansereau, D. F., & Rowan-Szal, G. A. (2001). Relationships between counseling rapport and drug abuse outcomes. *Psychiatric Services, 52*, 1223–1229.

Johns Hopkins University. (2008). *Facts about substance use.* Retrieved November 16, 2008, from the Innovators Combating Substance Abuse Web site: www.innovatorsawards.org/facts

Johnson, C. L. (2006). An innovative healing model: Empowering urban Native Americans. In T. M. Witko (Ed.), *Mental health care for urban Indians: Clinical insights from Native practitioners* (pp. 189–204). Washington, DC: American Psychological Association.

Johnson, D. W., & Johnson, F. P. (2006). *Joining together: Group theory and group skills.* Boston: Pearson.

Kadden, R. M., & Cooney, N. L. (2005). Treating alcohol problems. In G. A. Marlatt & D. M. Donovan (Eds.), *Relapse prevention: Maintenance strategies in the treatment of addictive behaviors* (2nd ed., pp. 65–91). New York: Guilford Press.

Kasarabada, N. D., Hser, Y., Boles, S. M., & Yu, C. H. (2002). Do patients' perceptions of their counselors influence outcomes of drug treatment? *Journal of Substance Abuse Treatment, 23*, 327–334.

Kellerman, J. L. (1969). *Alcoholism: A merry-go-round named denial.* Virginia Beach, VA: Al-Anon Family Group Headquarters.

Kelly, V. A., & Juhnke, G. A. (2005). *Critical incidents in addictions counseling.* Alexandria, VA: American Counseling Association.

Kessler, R. C., Crum, R. M., Warner, L. A., Nelson, C. B., Schulenberg, J., & Anthony, J. C. (1997). Lifetime co-occurrence of *DSM–III–R* alcohol abuse and dependence with other psychiatric disorders in the National Comorbidity Survey. *Archives of General Psychiatry, 54*, 313–321.

Kline, W. B. (2003). *Interactive group counseling and therapy.* Upper Saddle River, NJ: Prentice Hall.

Lambert, M. J., & Barley, D. E. (2002). Research summary on the therapeutic relationship and psychotherapy outcome. In J. C. Norcross (Ed.), *Psychotherapy relationships that work: Therapist contributions and responsiveness to patients* (pp. 17–32). New York: Oxford University Press.

Lee, M. L., Law, F. M., & Eo, E. (2003). Perceptions of substance use problems in Asian American communities by Chinese, Indian, Korean, and Vietnamese populations. *Journal of Ethnicity and Substance Abuse, 2,* 1–29.

Levine, J. D. (1993). *The dynamics and treatment of alcoholism.* North Vale, NJ: Aronson.

Malcolm, B. P., Hesselbrock, H. M., & Segal, B. (2006). Multiple substance dependence and course of alcoholism among Alaskan Native American men and women. *Substance Use and Misuse, 41,* 729–741.

Marlatt, G. A. (1985). Relapse prevention: Theoretical rationale and overview of the model. In G. A. Martlatt & J. Gordon (Eds.), *Relapse prevention: Maintenance strategies in the treatment of addictive behaviors* (pp. 3–70). New York: Guilford Press.

Martino, S., Carroll, K. M., Kostas, D., Perkins, J., & Rounsaville, B. (2002). Dual diagnosis motivational interviewing: A modification of motivational interviewing for substance abusing patients with psychotic disorders. *Journal of Substance Abuse Treatment, 23,* 297–308.

McIntyre, J. R. (1993). Family treatment of substance abuse. In S. L. A. Straussner (Ed.), *Clinical work with substance-abusing clients* (pp. 171–195). New York: Guilford Press.

Meyers, R. J., Miller, W. R., Smith, J. E., & Tonigan, J. S. (2002). A randomized trial of two methods for engaging treatment-refusing drug users through concerned significant others. *Journal of Consulting and Clinical Psychology, 70,* 1182–1185.

Miller, G. (2005). *Learning the language of addiction counseling* (2nd ed.). Hoboken, NJ: Wiley.

Miller, W. R., Meyers, R. J., & Tonigan, J. S. (1999). Engaging the unmotivated in treatment for alcohol problems: A comparison of three strategies for intervention through family members. *Journal of Consulting and Clinical Psychology, 67,* 688–697.

Miller, W. R., & Rollnick, S. (1991). *Motivational interviewing: Preparing people for change.* New York: Guilford Press.

Miller, W. R., & Rollnick, S. (2002). *Motivational interviewing: Preparing people for change* (2nd ed.). New York: Guilford Press.

Miller, W. R., Sorensen, J. L., Selzer, J. A., & Brigham, J. S. (2006). Disseminating evidence-based practices in substance abuse treatment: A review with suggestions. *Journal of Substance Abuse Treatment, 31,* 25–39.

Monti, P. M., Kadden, R. M., Rohsenow, D. J., Cooney, N. L., & Abrams, D. B. (2002). *Treating alcohol dependence: A coping skills training guide.* New York: Guilford Press.

Moos, R. (2007). Theory-based active ingredients of effective treatments for substance use disorders. *Drug and Alcohol Dependence, 88,* 109–121.

Morgenstern, J., & McKay, J. R. (2007). Rethinking the paradigms that inform behavioral treatment research for substance abuse disorders. *Addiction, 102,* 1377–1389.

Mueser, K. T., Noordsy, D. L., Drake, R. E., & Fox, L. (2003). *Integrated treatment for dual disorders.* New York: Guilford Press.

NAADAC, the Association for Addiction Professionals. (2008). *NAADAC code of ethics.* Retrieved November 29, 2008, from http://naadac.org/index.php?option=com_content&view=article&id=405&Itemid=73

Najavits, L. M., Crits-Christoph, P., & Dierberger, A. (2000). Clinicians' impact on the quality of substance use disorder treatment. *Substance Use and Misuse, 35,* 2161–2190.

National Association of State Alcohol and Drug Abuse Directors. (2008). *Guidance to states: Treatment standards for women with substance use disorders.* Retrieved January 20, 2009, from www.nasadad.org/resource.php?base_id=1482

Prochaska, J. O. (1999). How do people change, and how can we change to help many more people? In M. A. Hubble, B. L. Duncan, & S. D. Miller (Eds.), *The heart and soul of change: What works in therapy* (pp. 227–255). Washington, DC: American Psychological Association.

Prochaska, J. O., DiClemente, C. C., & Norcross, J. C. (1992). In search of how people change: Applications to addictive behaviors. *American Psychologist, 47,* 1102–1114.

Regier, D. A., Farmer, M. E., Rae, D. S., Locke, B. Z., Keith, S. J., Judd, L. L., et al. (1990). Comorbidity of mental disorders with alcohol and other drug abuse: Results from the Epidemiological Catchment Area study. *Journal of the American Medical Association, 264,* 2511–2518.

Rodriguez, E. O. (2005, June). Revisiting the alcoholic family: An integration of psychodynamic and 12-step oriented theory. *Counselor, 6,* 14–19.

Rogers, C. R. (1965). *Client-centered therapy.* Boston: Houghton Mifflin.

Rogers, C. R. (1992). The necessary and sufficient conditions of therapeutic personality change. *Journal of Consulting and Clinical Psychology, 60,* 827–832.

Ross, C. A., & Durkin, V. (2005). Childhood trauma, dissociation, and alcohol/other drug abuse among lesbian women. *Alcoholism Treatment Quarterly, 23,* 99–105.

Sellman, J. D., MacEwan, I. K., Deering, D. D., & Adamson, S. J. (2007). A comparison of motivational interviewing with non-directive counseling. In G. Tober & D. Raistrick (Eds.), *Motivational dialog: Preparing addiction professionals for motivational interviewing practice* (pp. 137–150). New York: Routledge.

Skinner, H. A. (1982). The Drug Abuse Screening Test. *Addictive Behaviors, 7,* 363–371.

Smith, J. E., & Meyers, R. J. (2004). *Motivating substance abusers to enter treatment: Working with family members.* New York: Guilford Press.

Steinglass, P., Davis, D. I., & Berenson, D. (1977). Observations of conjointly hospitalized "alcoholic couples" during sobriety and intoxication: Implications for theory and therapy. *Family Process, 16,* 1–16.

Straus, M. A., Hamby, S. L., & McCoy, S. (1996). The Revised Conflict Tactics Scales (CTS2): Development and preliminary psychometric data. *Journal of Family Issues, 17,* 283–316.

Straussner, S. L. (2003). Assessment and treatment of clients with alcohol and other drug abuse problems: An overview. In S. L. Straussner (Ed.), *Clinical work with substance-abusing clients* (pp. 3–35). New York: Guilford Press.

Sue, D. W., & Sue, D. (2008). *Counseling the culturally diverse: Theory and practice* (5th ed.). Hoboken, NJ: Wiley.

Sue, S., & Lam, A. G. (2002). Cultural and demographic diversity. In J. C. Norcross (Ed.), *Psychotherapy relationships that work: Therapist contributions and responsiveness to patients* (pp. 401–421). New York: Oxford University Press.

Tallman, K., & Bohart, A. C. (1999). The client as a common factor: Clients as self-healers. In M. A. Hubble, B. L. Duncan, & S. D. Miller (Eds.), *The heart and soul of change: What works in therapy* (pp. 91–131). Washington, DC: American Psychological Association.

Venner, K. L., Feldstein, S. W., & Tafoya, N. (2007). Helping clients feel welcome: Principles of adapting treatment cross-culturally. *Alcoholism Treatment Quarterly, 25,* 11–30.

Vereen, L. G., Hill, N. R., & McNeal, D. T. (2008). Perceptions of multicultural competency: Integration of the curricular and the practical. *Journal of Mental Health Counseling, 30,* 226–236.

Villanueva, M., Tonnigan, J. S., & Miller, W. R. (2007). Response of Native American clients to three treatment methods for alcohol dependence. *Journal of Ethnicity and Substance Abuse, 6,* 41–48.

Ward, D. E. (1984). Termination of individual counseling: Concepts and strategies. *Journal of Counseling & Development, 63,* 21–25.

Weber, G. N. (2008). Using to numb the pain: Substance use and abuse among lesbian, gay, and bisexual individuals. *Journal of Mental Health Counseling, 30,* 31–48.

Welfel, E. R. (2006). *Ethics in counseling and psychotherapy* (3rd ed.). Belmont, CA: Brooks/Cole.

Whalen, T. (1953). Wives of alcoholics: Four types observed in a family service agency. *Quarterly Journal of Studies on Alcohol, 14,* 632–641.

Yalisove, D. (2004). *Introduction to alcohol research: Implications for treatment, prevention, and policy.* Boston: Allyn & Bacon.

The Counseling Competencies of Technical Assistance Publication Series (TAP) 21 Covered in the Text

In all, TAP 21 lists 123 substance abuse counseling competencies; 66 are partially or completely covered in the text. Those covered or partially covered are listed below in italics along with the chapter in which they are discussed. Competencies include knowledge, skills, and attitude components. If a specific competency is only partially covered in the text, those elements covered are listed.

Transdisciplinary Foundation (TF) I: Understanding Addiction

(Competencies 1–4)

TF II: Treatment Knowledge

(Competencies 5–8)

- Competency 8: *Understand the value of an interdisciplinary approach to addiction treatment.* Chapter 10 discusses integrated treatment, an interdisciplinary approach. Role-play group exercises throughout text help students develop collaborative skill.

TF III: Applications to Practice

(Competencies 9–17)

- Competency 9: *Understand the established diagnostic criteria for substance use disorders, and describe treatment modalities and placement criteria within the continuum of care.* Diagnostic criteria are discussed in Chapter 2.

- Competency 10: *Describe a variety of helping strategies for reducing the negative effects of substance use, abuse, and dependence.* An array of helping strategies are discussed throughout the text. Chapter 4 in particular lists many helping strategies.
- Competency 11: *Tailor helping strategy to the various stages of dependence, change, and recovery.* Chapter 2 discusses the stages of change and the eight stages of counseling.
- Competency 12: *Provide treatment services appropriate to the personal and cultural identity and language of the client.* See Chapter 12.
- Competency 17: *Understand the need for and the use of methods for measuring treatment outcome.* Chapter 4 discusses evaluating the outcome of a session. Criteria for termination are discussed in Chapter 8.
- Competency 18: *Understand diverse cultures, and incorporate relevant needs of culturally diverse groups, as well as people with disabilities, into clinical practice.* See Chapter 12.

TF IV: Professional Readiness

(Competencies 18–23)

- Competency 19: *Understanding the importance of self-awareness in one's personal, professional, and cultural life.* Self-reflection is a key concept of the text and an important component of the exercises. It is discussed most fully in Chapter 5; cultural aspects are discussed in Chapter 12.
- Competency 21: *Understanding the importance of ongoing supervision and continuing education in the delivery of client services.* Chapter 14 addresses the importance of ongoing supervision and resources available for continuing education.

Practice Dimension (PD) I: Clinical Evaluation

(Competencies 24–36)

- Competency 24: *Establish rapport, including management of a crisis situation and determination of need for additional professional assistance.* Chapters 2–5 discuss various elements of this competency.
- Competency 25: *Gather data systematically from client and other sources.* Administration, scoring, and interpretation of the Alcohol Use Disorders Identification Test are addressed in Chapter 5. The psychosocial evaluation is discussed in Chapter 13, along with other issues of documentation.
- Competency 27: *Assist the client in identifying the effect of substance abuse. Skills: Establishing a therapeutic relationship* is discussed in Chapter 1 and throughout the text. *Demonstrating effective communication and interviewing skills* is discussed in the first five chapters. Relevant to *assessing the client's readiness to address substance abuse issues*, the stages of change and the eight stages of therapy are discussed in Chapter 2.

Respect for client's perception of his or her experiences is a key principle of motivational interviewing and is discussed in Chapter 2.

- Competency 28: *Determining the client's readiness for treatment and change.* The stages of change are discussed in Chapter 2.
- Competency 31: *Construct with the client an appropriate initial action plan.* Chapter 5 reviews this process.
- Competency 33: *Comprehensive assessment process.* Psychosocial evaluation is discussed in Chapter 13.
- Competency 35: *Seek appropriate supervision and consultation. Knowledge: The counselor's role, responsibilities, and scope of practice. The limits of the counselor's training and education. Skills: Providing appropriate documentation. Communicating oral and written information clearly.* The role and scope of practice of the counselor are discussed in Chapter 1. Chapter 10 discusses the role of the substance abuse counselor in dual diagnosis programs, including the need for additional education in mental health. Both Chapter 7 and Chapter 12 discuss the limits of substance abuse counseling in treating mental disorders. Documentation and communication are discussed in Chapter 13.
- Competency 36: *Documentation.* Chapter 13 discusses documentation.

PD II: Treatment Planning

(Competencies 37–48)

- Competency 37: *Use appropriate information to guide treatment planning.* Chapter 13 discusses treatment planning.
- Competency 38: *Explain assessment findings to client.* The text and exercises in Chapter 5 relate to this competency.
- Competency 39: *Provide clarification and explanation.* The discussion of rationales in Chapter 3 pertains to this competency.
- Competency 40: *Examine treatment options. Skills: Considering the client's needs and preferences* is discussed in Chapter 5, especially in the section on problem solving when the counselor and client have different goals. *Using the treatment planning process to foster collaborative relationships with the client and significant others.* Chapter 13 discusses the usefulness of collaboration with the client in the construction of a treatment plan.
- Competency 41: *Consider readiness of client to participate in treatment.* Chapter 2 discusses the stages of change.
- Competency 42: *Prioritize treatment needs.* This is considered in Chapters 3 and 13.
- Competency 43: *Measurable treatment goals.* This is discussed in Chapters 4 and 13.
- Competency 44: *Appropriate strategies for treatment goals.* This is discussed in Chapters 4 and 13.
- Competency 46: *Develop treatment plan and method of monitoring.* This is discussed in Chapter 13.

PD III: Referral

(Competencies 49–55)

- Competency 53: *Explain in clear and specific language the necessity for and the process of referral to increase the likelihood of client understanding and follow-through.* Chapter 3 discusses developing a rationale for any intervention, which includes referral. Chapter 4 discusses a strategy for increasing referral compliance.

PD IV: Service Coordination

(Competencies 56–74)

- Competency 60: *Establish treatment and recovery expectations.* Chapter 3 discusses how to help the client understand his or her role in the recovery process.
- Competency 62: *Summarize client's cultural and personal background. Skills: Client satisfaction, feedback* (see Chapter 5), *prioritizing* (see Chapters 3 and 13).
- Competency 63: *Understand terminology, role of other disciplines in treating substance abuse.* Chapter 10 discusses the role played by other disciplines in the treatment of dual disorders.
- Competency 64: *Contribute as a part of a multidisciplinary team.* Chapter 10 discusses the importance of collaboration as a part of a multidisciplinary team in the treatment of dual disorders. Team exercises throughout the text illustrate the importance of collaboration.
- Competency 68: *Understand stages of change and treatment progress.* Chapter 2 discusses the stages of change. Chapter 7 addresses the differences between clients who are making progress and those who are not and the appropriate counselor role for each status.
- Competency 69: *Document treatment progress and outcome.* Chapter 13 discusses documentation.
- Competency 71: *Use accepted outcome measures.* Chapter 8 discusses termination criteria for substance abuse clients.
- Competency 72: *Conduct continuing care, relapse prevention, and discharge planning.* Chapter 7 discusses relapse prevention. Chapter 8 addresses how to help the client envision recovery after treatment. Chapter 13 discusses aftercare and discharge planning.

PD V: Counseling

(Competencies 75–98)

- Competency 75: *Establish a helping relationship with the client characterized by warmth, respect, genuineness, concreteness, and empathy.* Chapter 2 introduces these topics. Chapter 5 applies the principles to the first session.

- Competency 76: *Facilitate the client's engagement in the treatment and recovery process.* Chapter 7 discusses how to evaluate the client's engagement and what to do if the client is not engaged as well as how to proceed when the client is engaged.
- Competency 77: *Work with the client to establish realistic, achievable goals, consistent with achieving and maintaining recovery.* Chapter 5 discusses session goals, and Chapter 13 discusses treatment goals.
- Competency 78: *Promote client knowledge, skills, and attitudes that contribute to a positive change in substance abuse behaviors.* Knowledge: *Stages of change model* (see Chapter 2). Skills: *Motivational techniques, client strengths, provide feedback on progress, coaching, recognizing and addressing resistance and ambivalence* (see Chapter 2). Attitudes: *Genuine care and concern for client* (see Chapter 2). *Appreciation of incremental progress* (see the *Break Goals Into Manageable Steps* section of Chapter 4; Chapter 10 discusses the importance of manageable steps for dual diagnosis clients). *Autonomy of client* (see Chapters 2 and 8).
- Competency 79: *Encourage and reinforce client actions determined to be beneficial in reaching treatment goals.* Knowledge: *Relapse prevention;* Skills: *Behavioral and cognitive methods* (see Chapter 6). Attitudes: *Autonomy* (see Chapters 2 and 8) *and incremental progress* (see Chapters 4 and 10).
- Competency 80: *Discourage behaviors inconsistent with recovery.* This topic is addressed in Chapter 5, especially in the section that discusses strategies to use when the counselor and client have different goals. Chapter 7 discusses evaluating the client's current lifestyle for its compatibility with recovery.
- Competency 83: *Facilitate the development of basic and life skills associated with recovery.* Chapter 7 discusses helping the client develop a lifestyle consistent with recovery.
- Competency 84: *Adapt counseling strategies to the individual characteristics of the client, including but not limited to disability, gender, sexual orientation, developmental level, culture, ethnicity, age, and health status.* See Chapter 12.
- Competency 85: *Make constructive therapeutic responses when the client's behavior is inconsistent with stated recovery goals.* Chapter 5 discusses what to do when the client's goals are different from the counselor's. Chapter 7 addresses how to discuss with the client when his or her lifestyle is not consistent with recovery.
- Competency 87: *Facilitate the client's identification, selection, and practice of strategies that help sustain the knowledge, skills, and attitudes needed for maintaining treatment progress and preventing relapse.* Chapter 8 examines the termination process, including a full discussion of the issues that must be addressed when the client continues on his or her own.
- Competency 88: *Describe, select, and appropriately use strategies from accepted and culturally appropriate models for group counseling with clients with substance use disorder.* See Chapter 9.

- Competency 89: *Carry out the actions necessary to form a group, including but not limited to determining group type, purpose, size, and leadership; recruiting and selecting members; establishing group goals and clarifying behavioral ground rules for participating; identifying outcomes; and determining criteria and methods for termination or graduation from the group.* See Chapter 9.
- Competency 90: *Facilitate the entry of new members and the transition of existing members.* See Chapter 9.
- Competency 91: *Facilitate group growth within the established ground rules and movement toward group and individual goals by using methods consistent with group type.* See Chapter 9.
- Competency 92: *Understand the concepts of process and content, and shift the focus of the group when such a shift will help the group move toward its goals.* See Chapter 9.
- Competency 93: *Describe and summarize the client's behavior within the group to document the client's progress and identify needs and issues that may require a modification to the treatment plan.* See Chapter 13.
- Competency 94: *Understand the characteristics and dynamics of families, couples, and significant others affected by substance use.* See Chapter 11.
- Competency 95: *Be familiar with and appropriately use models of diagnosis and intervention for families, couples, and significant others, including extended, kinship, or tribal family structure. Knowledge: Intervention strategies appropriate for violence against persons.* Chapter 11 discusses developing a safety plan. *Attitudes: Appreciation for the diversity found in families, couples, and significant others.* See Chapter 11.
- Competency 96: *Facilitate the engagement of selected members of the family or significant others in the treatment and recovery process.* See Chapter 11.
- Competency 97: *Assist families, couples, and significant others in understanding the interaction between the family system and substance use behaviors.* See Chapter 11.
- Competency 98: *Assist families, couples, and significant others in adopting strategies and behaviors that sustain recovery and maintain healthy relationships.* See Chapter 11.

PD VI: Client, Family, and Community Education

(Competencies 99–107)

PD VII: Documentation

(Competencies 108–114)

- Competency 108: *Demonstrate knowledge of accepted principles of client record management.* Chapter 13 discusses documentation.
- Competency 110: *Prepare accurate and concise screening, intake, and assessment reports.* Chapter 13 discusses these documents.

- Competency 111: *Record treatment and continuing care plans that are consistent with agency standards and comply with administrative rules.* Chapter 13 discusses treatment plans.
- Competency 112: *Record progress of client in relation to treatment goals and objectives.* Chapter 13 discusses progress notes.
- Competency 113: *Prepare accurate and concise discharge summaries.* Chapter 13 provides an example of a discharge summary.
- Competency 114: *Document treatment outcome, using accepted measures and instruments.* Chapter 13 provides an example of a discharge summary.

PD VIII: Professional and Ethical Responsibilities

(*Competencies 115–123*)

- Competency 117: *Interpret and apply information from current counseling and psychoactive substance use research literature to improve client care and to enhance professional growth.* This is discussed in Chapter 14.
- Competency 119: *Supervisory options. Knowledge: Problem-solving methods* (see Chapters 5 and 6), *effect of termination* (see Chapter 8), *stages of change* (see Chapter 2).
- Competency 120: *Conduct self-evaluations.* Chapters 2 and 5 and exercises throughout the text discuss the importance of self-evaluations and how to conduct them.
- Competency 121: *Obtain appropriate continuing professional education.* Chapter 14 provides guidance on this topic.

Note. The TAP 21 competencies are reprinted from *Addiction Counseling Competencies: The Knowledge, Skills, and Attitudes of Professional Practice* (TAP Series 21, DHHS Publication No. SMA 06-4171), by the Center for Substance Abuse Treatment, 2006, Rockville, MD: Substance Abuse and Mental Health Services Administration.

Appendix B

Role-Play Recording Form
and Instructions

For those who wish to perform the role-play exercises, I have developed the following instructions and format.

The purpose of recording your role-plays is to help you develop *self-reflective skills*. In role-playing the counselor, you can observe the areas in which you feel comfortable and competent and the areas in which you feel uncomfortable, hesitant, or unskilled. The instructor will help you develop skills in these areas. You will learn about the client's perspective when role-playing a client. This can help you develop empathy. Think of the workbook log as an opportunity to write down your impressions, your strengths, your weaknesses, and your insights when participating in the role-plays.

The log should include not only what you and your partner said but your emotional reactions, thoughts, and so on. It is more important to talk about your genuine reactions than to indicate that the role-play was great. The path to good counseling typically requires even the best students to make many mistakes. Our willingness to acknowledge them is the first step to overcoming them.

Before beginning the role-play, complete Part 1.

Part 1: Set-Up for the Role-Play

Date of role-play:

Names of participants and assignments:

Name of case study (if based on one):

Description of scenario (so instructor can easily identify the role-play):

Statement of problem (What is the client concerned about? What other concerns should be addressed?):

Goals of session:

Techniques to be used:

Part 2: Verbatim Record of the Role-Play

The *verbatim record* of the role-play is a detailed description of the actual unfolding of the scenario. While the role-play is going on, the recorders write a detailed account of what the participants say and their emotional reactions. One of the recorders must then put the counselor's comments together with the client's comments to form a dialogue. Keep track of the techniques used as well, by underlining and labeling them.

Immediately after a team role-play, the team members should discuss their experiences in the role-play. How did the student role-playing the counselor feel? What did he or she observe? Similarly, what did the student role-playing the client feel and observe? A summary of this discussion should be included as part of the verbatim account.

Part 3: Discussion of the Role-Play

After the role-play is concluded, make an evaluation of the role-play:

Were goals achieved?

Why or why not?

Were techniques used?

How often?

Were they used skillfully? How so?

Were they therapeutic? Why?

What did you learn from watching the role-play and analyzing the transcript you created? You can draw on the reactions of the client and the counselor and on your own personal reactions. You can go beyond the goals, the techniques, and the structure of this form for these comments.

What question did this role-play raise in your mind about substance abuse counseling?

Part 4: Individual Student Analysis and Discussion

On your own, underline key elements of the dialogue, and discuss them with your team or in class. For example, if you are to use reflection in the exercise, underline all of the reflections in the dialogue. Also underline noteworthy reactions of the student role-playing the client. Underline all noteworthy comments in the dialogue, and then discuss them with your team or classmates.

Alcohol Use Disorders Identification Test (AUDIT) and Drug Abuse Screening Test (DAST-20)

The AUDIT, Interview Version

Instructions: Read questions as written. Record answers carefully. Begin the AUDIT by saying, "Now I am going to ask you some questions about your use of alcoholic beverages during the past year." Explain what is meant by "alcoholic beverages" by using local examples of beer, wine, vodka, etc. Code answers in terms of "standard drinks." Place the correct number answer in the space at the left.

_____   1. How often do you have a drink containing alcohol?
            (0) Never. [*Skip to Questions 9–10.*]
            (1) Monthly or less.
            (2) 2 to 4 times a month.
            (3) 2 to 3 times a week.
            (4) 4 or more times a week.

_____   2. How many drinks containing alcohol do you have on a typical day when you are drinking?
            (0) 1 or 2.
            (1) 3 or 4.
            (2) 5 or 6.
            (3) 7, 8, or 9.
            (4) 10 or more.

_____ 3. How often do you have 6 or more drinks on one occasion?
    (0) Never.
    (1) Less than monthly.
    (2) Monthly.
    (3) Weekly.
    (4) Daily or almost daily.

Skip to Questions 9 and 10 if Total Score for Questions 2 and 3 = 0.

_____ 4. How often during the last year have you found that you were not able to stop drinking once you had started?
    (0) Never.
    (1) Less than monthly.
    (2) Monthly.
    (3) Weekly.
    (4) Daily or almost daily.

_____ 5. How often during the last year have you failed to do what was normally expected from you because of drinking?
    (0) Never.
    (1) Less than monthly.
    (2) Monthly.
    (3) Weekly.
    (4) Daily or almost daily.

_____ 6. How often during the last year have you needed a first drink in the morning to get yourself going after a heavy drinking session?
    (0) Never.
    (1) Less than monthly.
    (2) Monthly.
    (3) Weekly.
    (4) Daily or almost daily.

_____ 7. How often during the last year have you had a feeling of guilt or remorse after drinking?
    (0) Never.
    (1) Less than monthly.
    (2) Monthly.
    (3) Weekly.
    (4) Daily or almost daily.

_____ 8. How often during the last year have you been unable to remember what happened the night before because you were drinking?
(0) Never.
(1) Less than monthly.
(2) Monthly.
(3) Weekly.
(4) Daily or almost daily.

_____ 9. Have you or someone else been injured as a result of your drinking?
(0) No.
(2) Yes. But not in the past year.
(4) Yes. During the past year.

_____ 10. Has a relative, a friend, or a doctor or another health worker been concerned about your drinking or suggested you cut down?
(0) No.
(2) Yes. But not in the past year.
(4) Yes. During the past year.

Record total of specific items here: _____

(Add each number next to the answer selected. For example, if the answer selected in Question 10 is "Yes. During the past year," the item is scored 4. Add the scores for the 10 items to get a total score.)

A score of 8 or more will include almost all of the persons with an alcohol disorder but will include a small percentage of those without alcohol disorders (high sensitivity). A score of 10 or more may miss a small percentage of those with alcohol disorders but will include fewer without alcohol disorders (high specificity). (See Babor, Biddle, Saunders, & Monteiro, 2001, for further details on administration, scoring, and interpretation.)

The DAST-20

Although this test was designed to be self-administered, I recommend that students pose the questions to a client in a role-play. Some of the questions are challenging to ask in a neutral manner. The student administering the test should note the response of the student role-playing the client.

Administration

The DAST should not be administered to clients who are currently under the influence of drugs or who are undergoing a drug withdrawal reaction. It is recommended that the DAST be used as a self-administered test, using the following instructions:

The following questions concern information about your potential involvement with drugs, not including alcoholic beverages, during the past 12 months. Carefully read each statement and decide if your answer is "yes" or "no." Then circle the appropriate response beside the question. In the statement, "drug abuse" refers to (1) the use of prescribed or over the counter drugs in excess of the directions and (2) any nonmedical use of drugs. The various classes of drugs may include: cannabis (marijuana, hash), solvents, tranquilizers (e.g., Valium), barbiturates, cocaine, stimulants (e.g., speed), hallucinogens (e.g., LSD), or narcotics (e.g., heroin). Remember that the questions *do not* include alcoholic beverages.

Please answer every question. If you have difficulty with a statement, then choose the statement that is mostly right.

Adult Version

These questions refer to the past 12 months.   *Circle Your Response*

1. Have you used drugs other than those required for medical reasons? — Yes   No
2. Have you abused prescription drugs? — Yes   No
3. Do you abuse more than one drug at a time? — Yes   No
4. Can you get through the week without using drugs? — Yes   No
5. Are you always able to stop using drugs when you want to? — Yes   No
6. Have you ever had "blackouts" or "flashbacks" as a result of drug use? — Yes   No
7. Do you ever feel bad or guilty about your drug use? — Yes   No
8. Does your spouse (or parents) ever complain about your involvement with drugs? — Yes   No
9. Has drug abuse created problems between you and your spouse or your parents? — Yes   No
10. Have you lost friends because of your drug use? — Yes   No
11. Have you neglected your family because of your use of drugs? — Yes   No
12. Have you been in trouble at work (or school) because of drug abuse? — Yes   No
13. Have you lost your job because of drug abuse? — Yes   No
14. Have you gotten into fights when under the influence of drugs? — Yes   No
15. Have you engaged in illegal activities in order to obtain drugs? — Yes   No
16. Have you been arrested for possession of illegal drugs? — Yes   No
17. Have you ever experienced withdrawal symptoms (felt sick) when you stopped taking drugs? — Yes   No

18. Have you had medical problems as a result of your
    drug use (e.g., memory loss, hepatitis, convulsions,
    bleeding, etc.)?   Yes   No
19. Have you gone to anybody for help with your
    drug problem?   Yes   No
20. Have you been involved in a treatment program
    specifically related to drug use?   Yes   No

Scoring

The DAST total score is computed by summing all items that are endorsed in the direction of increased drug problems. Two items, #4 ("Can you get through the week without using drugs?") and #5 ("Are you always able to stop using drugs when you want to?"), are keyed for a "No" response. The other 18 items are keyed for a "Yes" response. For example, if a client circled "Yes" for item #1, he/she would receive a score of 1, whereas if a client circled "No" for item #1, he/she would receive a score of 0. With items #4 and 5, a score of 1 would be given for a "No" response and a score of 0 for a "Yes" response. When each item has been scored in this fashion, the DAST *total score* is simply the sum of the 20 item scores. This total score can range from 0 to 20.

Interpretation

A DAST score of *6 or greater* is suggested for case finding purposes (i.e., the client should receive a full assessment for a possible drug use disorder).

Note: The AUDIT is from *AUDIT: Alcohol Use Disorders Identification Test: Guidelines for Use in Primary Care* (2nd ed.), by T. F. Babor, J. C. Biddle, J. B. Saunders, and M. G. Monteiro, 2001, Geneva, Switzerland: World Health Organization. Available at http://whqlibdoc.who.int/hq/2001/WHO_MSD_MSB_01.6a.pdf. Copyright 2001 by the World Health Organization. The DAST-20 is from "The Drug Abuse Screening Test," H. A. Skinner, 1982, *Addictive Behaviors, 7,* 363–371. Copyright 1982 by Harvey A. Skinner, PhD, and the Centre for Addiction and Mental Health, Toronto, Canada.

Index

Index

Interrupted use, 13
   See also Relapse
Interviewing. *See* Motivational interviewing
   (MI)
Intoxicated or high client
   See also Drug usage, determination of
   role-playing of, 40
   in violation of agency policy, 74, 78
Introduction to Alcohol Research (Yalisove),
   164
Islamic beliefs, 131
Isolation issues, 118

J

Job survival, 161–162

K

Kempter, Richard, 81

L

Language and cultural differences, 130–132,
   138, 144
Lapse, 13
   See also Relapse
Latino/a clients, 135
Laws, adherence to, 164
Lesbians. *See* Gay, lesbian, bisexual, and
   transgendered (GLBT) clients
Life goals, 61, 64–65
Lifestyle
   balance in, 63
   GLBT, 141, 142
   as treatment issue, 61, 64–65
Listening, 31, 66, 94, 123, 124

M

Macho pride, 94
Maintenance stage, 13, 36*t*, 74
Malcolm, B. P., 135
Managed care, 74
Mandated clients, 55, 56–58, 59
Mandatory reporting, 164
Manipulation, 86
Marlatt, G. A., 63
Martino, S., 107, 108, 109
Measuring progress of client, 37, 40
Medication
   interactions with drug and alcohol
      use, 102
   monitoring compliance, 101–102, 106
   side effects of, 102

Medicine wheel, 136
Mental illness
   definition of, 99–100
   diagnosis of, 23
   monitoring symptoms of, 101, 103–104
   role-playing of clients with, 111–112
   serious mental illness (SMI), 100, 103
   substance abuse users with, 99–112
      See also Dual disorder clients
   treatment support, 102
   types of, 100
Mentally ill chemical abuse (MICA)
   programs, 100
Mental status, defined, 146
Metaphors, use by counselors, 31, 130
Methadone maintenance programs, 3, 139
Meyers, R. J., 120
MI. *See* Motivational interviewing
MICA (Mentally ill chemical abuse)
   programs, 100
Middle phase of treatment, 17, 61–69
   coping skills, 63
   factors related to substance abuse and,
      66
   lifestyle, goals, and career examina-
      tion, 64–65
   relapse prevention, 62–63
   role change of counselor, 61–62
   termination anticipation, 66–67
   12-step and other self help approaches,
      63–64
   values clarification, 65
Mild to moderate mental illness, 100
Miller, S. D., 7
Miller, W. R., 10
Minorities. *See* Diversity issues
Modeling, 86
Moderation Management, 68
Monitoring
   in BSGS sessions, 32
   of medication compliance, 101–102, 106
   of mental health treatment, 102
   of symptoms in dual disorder clients,
      101, 103–104
Motivational interviewing (MI), 10–11
   ambivalence as element of, 11, 54
   defensiveness, how to avoid, 53
   diagnosis, client's acceptance of, 23
   dual disorder clients, modifications
      for, 107–109
   empathy as element of, 10–11
   Native Americans and, 137
   resources for, 166
   as therapeutic approach, 7

Motivational Interviewing Network of
Trainers, 166
Motivation of client
as BSGS technique, 30, 35–36*t*
building, 52–54
for continuing counseling, 47, 53
counselor's evaluation of, 15–16, 52–53
counselor's role in, 22
as critical MI principle, 11
Multicultural competence, 127, 128–129, 130, 131
Multicultural counseling, 127
See also Diversity issues
Multifamily counseling, 134
Multigenerational trauma cycle, 136
Mythology, 96

N

NA. *See* Narcotics Anonymous
NAADAC (National Association of
Alcoholism and Drug Abuse Counselors),
128, 163–164, 167
Web site, 167
Nar-Anon, 120
Narcotics Anonymous (NA), 3, 63–64, 165
Web site, 68
National Institute on Alcoholism and
Alcohol Abuse, 164
National Institute on Drug Addiction, 164
Native American church, 137
Native American clients, 132–133, 135–137
Negative thinking management, 63
Non-discrimination, 128, 163
Nonjudgmental attitude, 107, 115
Nonstranger counseling groups, 96–97
Noordsy, D. L., 100
Norcross, J. C., 12
Normalizing behavior, 32
Norms, defined, 92

O

Observation as group technique, 94–95, 97
Open-ended counseling groups, 96
Open-ended questions, 45, 50
Opening statement for new clients, 49
Openness, 32
Operational empathy, 32, 45
Oppression, 127–128, 136
Orientation of client, 43, 44

P

Paperwork, 4, 157
See also Clinical writing

Partial remission, 104
Patterns of behavior, 31
Personal character traits for counselors, 5–6
Personality disorders, 101
Personal mythology, 96
Persons with disabilities, 139–140, 144
Persuasion, 86, 105
Peyote, 137
Philosophy of treatment, 3
Physical appearance of clients, 139–140
"Pink cloud" feeling, 62
Plans, treatment, 150–155
Positive feedback. *See* Feedback
Positive reinforcement from CSO, 121–123
Posttraumatic stress disorder. *See* PTSD
Power issues, 92–94
Precontemplation stage, 12, 35*t*, 57, 58, 62, 74
Predetermined length of treatment, 74
Pregnant women, 134
Prejudice. *See* Discrimination
Premature termination, 69, 73–74, 79
Preparation for action stage, 12, 35–36*t*
Presenting problems, 146
Principles of substance abuse counseling, 21–25
boundary setting with clients, 22–23
diagnostic considerations, 23
education of client, 21–22
prioritization of issues, 24–25
time-limited sessions, 23–24
Prioritizing, 24–25
in BSGS sessions, 29–30, 32
case study review, 25
Problems of client
counselor anticipating, 16–17, 30, 76
counselor ascertaining, 14–15
counselor understanding, 15, 34, 45–46
presenting problem, 146
summary of, 50
Problem solving, 32, 46–47, 135
Prochaska, J. O., 12, 63
Professional organizations for substance
abuse counselors, 167
Professional practice of addiction counseling, 5
Progress notes, 145, 155–157, 160 (exhibit)
Progress of client, measurement of, 37, 40
Promoting self-efficacy, 54
Psychiatric disorders. *See* Dual disorder
clients; Mental illness
Psychological abuse, 118
Psychosocial evaluations, 145, 146
Psychosocial narratives
example of, 146, 149–150 (exhibit)